Efficient Sheep Production From Grass

Occasional Symposium No. 21, British Grassland Society

Proceedings of a Conference organised jointly with the
National Sheep Association held at
Harrogate, North Yorkshire
4–5 November 1986

Edited by
G. E. POLLOTT

BRITISH

GRASSLAND

SOCIETY

OCCASIONAL SYMPOSIUM NO. 21

British Grassland Society
Institute for Grassland and Animal Production
Hurley, Maidenhead,
Berkshire SL6 5LR, UK.

1987

ISBN 0 905944 13 5
ISSN 0572–7022

Printed in Great Britain
The Lavenham Press Limited, Lavenham, Suffolk

ACKNOWLEDGEMENTS

This conference was organised by a committee under the Chairmanship of Mr J. M. M. Munro consisting of members from both BGS and the National Sheep Association. Both BGS and NSA gratefully acknowledge all those who gave their time unstintingly to ensure the success of the conference. The organisers also gratefully acknowledge the support received from the following organisations in promoting this meeting:

Coopers Animal Health Ltd
ICI plc, Agricultural Division
Meat and Livestock Commission
Robert Young & Co Ltd

CONTENTS

vi

THE AIMS AND OBJECTIVES
OF THE BRITISH GRASSLAND SOCIETY

The aim is to provide a forum for all those with an active interest in the science and the practice of temperate grassland production and utilization by bringing together research workers, advisers, farmers and technical members of the agricultural industry.

The objectives of the Society are:

a) To encourage research and practice in all aspects of grassland and forage husbandy which will lead to improvements in the efficiency of its use.

b) To communicate as widely as possible the results of research and practice in grassland and forage crops.

Membership

This is open to all those with a keen interest in grassland and the furtherance of the Society's objectives.

Membership is drawn from research, the advisory service, agricultural education, farmers and allied interests.

There are over 60 local grassland societies which are affiliated to the BGS.

Publications

An international scientific journal, "Grass & Forage Science" is published quarterly and supplied to members free of charge. Three times each year, the Society publishes "Grass Farmer", which is practically orientated and gives reports of farm practices, together with research and development findings in digest form. This is also sent to members free of charge.

Other occasional publications include textbooks, symposia proceedings and reports of meeting and surveys.

Further information on any aspect of BGS can be obtained from:

> The Secretary
> British Grassland Society
> c/o Institute for Grassland and Animal Production
> Hurley
> Maidenhead SL6 5LR

THE NSA

The National Sheep Association is the organisation dedicated entirely to the interests of sheep farmers. It is run by practical farmers and represents the core of the sheep breeding industry.

The NSA acts as the parent body to all 65 purebred and half-bred Societies as well as commercial farmers. It helps to improve production by monitoring expenditure on research and development and to relate modern sheep production to today's market. It supports promotion of sheep meat as well as organising sheep events and sales, technical conferences, demonstrations and shows for the benefit of sheep farmers.

It exerts strong political pressure in the interests of sheep farmers both at home and in the EEC and publishes the only authoritative journal on sheep farming, the *Sheep Farmer*.

Further information about NSA can be obtained from:

The Secretary
National Sheep Association
106 High Street
Tring
Herts HP23 4AF

INVITED PAPERS

Economics and Market Outlook

G. E. POLLOTT
Meat and Livestock
Commission, PO Box 44,
Bletchley, Milton Keynes,
MK2 2EF

ABSTRACT

The economics of each flock depend on the farm structure of the holding on which they are kept. Results from MLC's Flockplan scheme show large between breed and system variation for a range of grassland and economic performance measures. The greatest source of variation in grassland performance is due to factors under the control of the flockmaster. Stocking rate and rearing percentage are the most important determinants of profitable production and the economic effect of improvements in these factors is discussed. The outlook for sheep meat production in the UK is dependent on future changes to the EEC sheepmeat regime. Current trends show increasing production, exports and consumption of home produced lamb and a decline in imports, market prices and consumer expenditure on lamb. Future margins are likely to be squeezed by little change in guide prices and an increase in costs. This effect will result in the need to improve the efficiency of production in order to remain profitable.

INTRODUCTION

Each sheep flock operates within a different set of farm objectives, balance of enterprises, fixed cost structure and cash flow profile. Despite this diversity there are two underlying features which are common to all flocks. The physical performance of each flock is a fundamental determinant of its profitability and all flocks operate within the wider context of the national economy, in particular the Common Agricultural Policy (CAP) of the European Economic Community. Both these aspects of sheep production are considered in this paper.

CURRENT PERFORMANCE LEVELS

Most of the results from British sheep flocks used in this paper are from records collected in commercial sheep flocks as part of the Meat and Livestock Commission's Flockplan scheme. It is pertinent at this stage to ask how representative of the industry at large is this sample of results. The data collected are part of a scheme designed to provide a sound basis for management advice and as such are not a random or structured sample of flocks in Britain.

1

Table 1.   Estimated national rearing percentage 1985

	MLC Flockplan	Proportion of ewe population	Estimated national rearing %		
			Flockplan	Census data*	From census data**
Lowland	148	0.40			140
Upland	131	0.17	127	110	125
Hill	105	0.43			75

June census plus lamb slaughterings January to May
**Sector estimates to give census data average*

The results for rearing percentage in Table 1 are an attempt to relate two different sources of the same information in order to assess the position of Flockplan results in the national picture. Using data from Flockplan (MLC, 1986a and b) and combining it with data from MAFF on the proportion of the national flock claiming Less Favoured Area (LFA) subsidies (see for example Croston and Pollott (1985)) suggests a national flock rearing percentage of 127. Data from the latest June and December censuses combined with certification data from January to May give a figure of 110%. Flockplan results are therefore from an above average sample of flocks and the final column in Table 1 shows the likely national rearing percentages in the three sectors; lowland, upland and hill.

Repeating this type of comparison for stocking density lowland results from Flockplan give an estimate of 2.72 livestock units (LSU)/ha and the census data estimate is 2.27 LSU/ha. Taking both sets of comparisons together Flockplan results would appear to be about 15–20% above crude estimates of the national average. Nevertheless Flockplan results provide a good basis for comparisons between a wide range of results from classifications such as breed, system and year. In addition they provide a valuable insight into the level of within-classification variation.

Breed and system performance

Average levels of flock performance in 1985 are shown in Tables 2 and 3 for four common lowland crossbreds and five production systems respectively (MLC, 1986a and b). Comparisons between the four crossbred types show differences in the performance variables summarised. However as the nitrogen data in Table 2 indicates there are a range of other factors which are affecting the results shown. Similar comments could be made about the extremely variable types of system shown in Table 3. The most surprising result of comparisons in Table 3 is the similarity between average performance levels in some extremely diverse situations. This investigation into the significance of breed and system in relation

Table 2. Lowland breed performance averages from Flockplan 1985

	Rearing %	Overall stocking rate (ewes/ha)	Gross margin (£)		Nitrogen use (kg/ha)
			Per ewe	Per ha	
Mule	159	11.6	31.50	364	169
Welsh Halfbred	142	12.2	33.10	409	146
Scottish Halfbred	144	12.2	30.56	373	158
Suffolk × Scottish Halfbred	134	12.2	24.89	310	141

NB: These are not direct breed comparisons but indications of breed performance on lowland farms.

Table 3. Results from a range of systems in 1985

	Lowland			Upland	
	Intensive early lambing	Spring lambs sold from grass	Hogget finishing	Grass and forage lambs	Crossbred lamb production from draft hill ewes
Rearing %	142	153	154	153	131
Overall stocking rate (ewes/ha)	18.9	13.0	10.5	10.0	11.3
Nitrogen use (kg/ha)	132	165	143	114	101
Gross margin/ewe (£)	25.07	33.42	33.89	38.52	39.01
Gross margin/ha (£)	474	434	356	385	441

to performance is taken further in Tables 4 and 5 by looking at some simple indicators of within-breed and system variation. In these tables the data have been ranked on each variable in turn to give top and bottom third averages.

A considerable amount of data on the performance of Mules (Blue Faced Leicester × Swaledale) on lowland farms has been collected in the Flockplan scheme. The range, top and bottom third and average results for rearing percentage and gross margin/ha are shown in Table 4. A much greater within-breed spread of performance is found than the between breed comparisons shown in Table 5 which indicates considerable within-system variation in grassland and financial performance.

Table 4. Performance variation within Mule flocks 1985

	Bottom third	Average	Top third	Range
Gross margin (£/ha)	203	364	535	7 to 918
Rearing %	128	159	179	89 to 205

Table 5. Lowland lambs from grass – within system variation

	Bottom third	Average	Top third	Range
Rearing %	123	148	174	86 to 206
Overall stocking rate	8.8	12.0	15.7	4.5 to 29.0
Gross margin/ewe (£)	19.70	31.06	42.22	−2.06 to 72.81
Gross margin/ha (£)	210	372	561	−30 to 918
Nitrogen use (kg/ha)	74	141	251	12 to 451

Performance from grass

The wide range in grassland performance found in Britain can be attributed to two main types of effect, environmental and management. Environmental factors are a function of the physical situation of the sheep enterprise and include rainfall, altitude, length of the grazing season, aspect, soil type and the fixed equipment available. Management factors are to a large extent under the control of the flockmaster and include system, feed use, breed, nitrogen use, conservation policy and the type of grassland available. The relative importance of these sets of effects are shown in Table 6 for five different measures of utilised output. These results are expressed as the proportion of the total variation in the five variables accounted for by the two sets of effects. In all cases the influence of management decisions on output far outweigh that of the uncontrollable environmental effects.

Table 6. The relative importance of environmental and management effects on five measures of utilised output (% of variation accounted for by class of effect)

	Environmental	Management
Liveweight carried/ha	6	44
Gross margin/ha	1	23
Summer stocking rate	4	41
Ewe live weight carried/ha	8	50
Lamb weight produced/ha	9	54

Another point of interest to arise from these figures is the amount of variation which has *not* been accounted for in terms of the usually stated factors which affect output. This unexplained variation will be discussed later in relation to the utilisation of resources.

Apart from the overall effect of management variables on output the magnitude of the individual effects is of interest. These are summarised in Table 7 for the most important effects using liveweight carried per hectare (LWC) as the measure of output. System of production had no effect on LWC. Lowland and upland production systems also produced similar output once differences in the factors shown in Table 6 were taken into account. The use of more nitrogen resulted in higher levels of output. On average the use of two extra bags of 34% N fertiliser per hectare resulted in increased stocking of 66 kg of liveweight/ha. Grassland areas used for conservation cuts as well as grazing supported 92 kg of liveweight less/ha than grazed-only areas. Output from an all-ley farm was higher than from an all-permanent pasture farm by 140 kg of liveweight/ha. The use of heavier ewes resulted in greater output from grass whilst flocks using an additional 10 kg of creep stocked 19 kg of live weight/ha more.

Table 7. The effect of management factors on liveweight carried (kg/ha)

An extra 34 kg nitrogen/ha	+ 66
Conservation taken from grassland	− 92
All ley compared to all permanent pasture	+140
75 kg ewe compared to 65 kg ewe	+ 28
Extra 10 kg of lamb creep fed	+ 19
No effect of system	
Lowland and upland output the same	

Economic performance

The wide range of physical performance found in British sheep flocks underlies the wide range of economic performance. Using the concept of top third performance as an indicator of good performance a summary of the important factors contributing to top third superiority are shown in Table 8 for lowland, upland and hill flocks (MLC, 1986a and b). Several conclusions can be drawn from this table.

Firstly it is physical performance which is the key to profitability in the form of stocking rate and rearing percentage. Secondly lamb sale price is relatively unimportant. Thirdly production costs per ewe are similar for both top third and average flocks. These general conclusions are different in the hill situation where the extensive nature of production focuses more on rearing percentage and lamb sale price than in the lowlands and uplands. Efficient sheep production from grass, in the economic sense, is achieved using a similar level of resources to give increased ewe and grassland performance.

Table 8. The contribution of flock performance factors to top
third superiority – 1985 (%)

	Lowland*	Upland*	Hill**
Overall stocking rate	40	48	—
Rearing %	25	42	44
Flock replacement cost	11	1	—
Lamb sale price/head	9	9	27
Feed and forage costs	8	−1	11
Draft ewe sale price	—	—	14
Others	7	1	4

Top third based on gross margin per hectare
**Top third based on gross margin per ewe*

IMPROVING EFFICIENCY AND ECONOMIC PERFORMANCE

Three of the possible routes to increased economic efficiency are the more efficient use of the resources currently employed, the use of a higher level of inputs and maintaining output with a lower level of inputs. The more efficient use of the resources employed has already been shown to have considerable influence on top third superiority and is often described in terms of 'a higher level of stockmanship'. In reality this is a combination of several successful husbandry techniques. Many of the papers in this book discuss the basis of these techniques.

Improved utilisation

In the present context of improving the efficiency of sheep production from grass the most obvious route to improved utilisation is through increasing stocking rate for a given set of conditions, including ewe breed and level of nitrogen use. The scope for improvement will depend on the present level of performance in relation to the optimum for any given situation. However results from MLC (1985) indicate that over the range of recorded flocks an increase of one ewe/ha is worth an extra £26.78 in gross margin/ha. Such an increase in stocking pressure during the year can be thought of in terms of changes in grass height.

Different levels of economic efficiency are found between flocks of ewes of different sizes (MLC, 1985). Smaller ewes produce higher gross margins per hectare. For every 10 kg reduction in ewe weight there is a concomitant rise in gross margin of £31.93/ha. Changing breeds is an expensive undertaking and should not be attempted without a full consideration of all the implications. However these results show that the rearing percentage achieved from smaller breeds is greater per unit of body size than that achieved by larger breeds. Provided that stocking rate is adjusted accordingly using smaller ewes should result in a higher gross margin/ha.

Several different management factors are expressed in the form of increased lamb growth rate. These include the use of clean grazing or a sound worm control programme, the use of a high-growth potential ram, the use of creep feed and efficient feeding of ewes during lactation. The economic effects of improving growth rate by any of these means will depend on the time of year that lambs are marketed. During early summer an increase in growth rate of 50 g/day can be worth nearly £3/ewe (MLC, 1986c). This is in addition to any benefits from reduced lamb deaths and increased stocking of ewes made possible by the earlier removal of lambs. These factors have been combined to produce the 'Bedford' system of lamb production which has already claimed three BGS/MLC Grass to Meat Awards. In this system lamb growth is maximised to such an extent that in many cases there is no scope for conservation until after the lambs have been sold. Land is then available for conservation due to the tightening-up of ewe stocking before flushing.

Further improvements in utilisation can be made by conserving young high quality grass. Silage cuts are the best way to achieve this. Early and repeated cuts are necessary rather than later cuts with a high volume/cut. The results shown in Table 9 compare the use of silage, hay and straw as the main source of winter forage (MLC, 1986a). The higher quality feeds prove more profitable.

Table 9. A comparison of flocks feeding silage, hay and straw

	Silage	Hay	Straw
Rearing %	147	148	139
Feed costs (£/ewe)	8.02	9.56	12.33
Forage costs (£/ewe)	7.08	6.33	6.46
Gross margin (£/ewe)	31.96	30.25	22.14

Increased output from increased inputs

The higher use of inputs will not in itself lead to extra output. The belief that it does may be the cause of much uneconomic production in the UK at present. However if inputs are currently being used at their optimum efficiency then improved economic efficiency may be achieved by using a higher level of inputs at the same level of efficiency.

Increased nitrogen use leads to lower gross margins unless the extra grass grown is used to produce more lamb. Records show that farms using 34 kg more nitrogen/ha increased gross margin/ha by £27.16 (MLC, 1985). At current prices this is a profitable change to make providing that the implications in terms of a higher ewe requirement or a reduced grazing area are budgeted well in advance.

Further improvements in output from a higher level of input may be achieved by using more concentrate feed. The successful use of these extra feed inputs is dependent on the timing of the additional input. The most important times are

7

during lactation, around mating time and in late pregnancy. The feeding of ewes to meet their requirements is essential and can lead to a more efficient grassland use. This is particularly the case in the early part of the grazing season when grass height can be used as an indicator of the need for concentrates. Later in the year food stocks should be managed to buffer the ewe and lamb against adverse effects on ewe condition or lamb growth.

Lower input systems

The scope for lower input systems is limited if margins are to be maintained. One particularly useful approach is the use of grass/clover swards. This would seem to be a method for reducing fertiliser costs whilst still achieving good output although few economic data from enterprises using this approach are available. However, if similar levels of output are possible to a grass sward receiving 200 kg of nitrogen/ha, as suggested by Newton and Davies (1987), then a saving of £60/ha in fertiliser cost seems possible.

MARKET TRENDS AND OUTLOOK

EEC sheep meat regime

Any discussion on market trends and the outlook for sheep producers cannot ignore the effects of the EEC sheep meat regime. It is estimated that in 1985 the financial support to the UK industry from the CAP budget was worth £15/ewe on average. This support is part of a package of measures which are summarised in Table 10.

Table 10. EEC support to British sheep industry

Ewe premium
Variable premium/clawback
Voluntary restraint agreements
Less favoured area payments (half)
Free trade within EEC

Direct support is available to all sheep producers, with over 10 ewes, in the form of the ewe premium. This was worth £7.32 in 1986. In addition producers in three classes of 'less favoured area' are eligible for £6.75, £4.50 or £2.25 in 1986 depending on the area. Further direct support is payable to anyone selling lambs for slaughter through the Sheep Variable Premium scheme. This scheme pays the difference between the average market price and the previously declared guide price for the week in which the lambs were presented for certification.

Two other measures are in force which can be of help to British farmers. Voluntary Restraint Agreements (VRA) have been made between the EEC and certain other countries setting the maximum amount of sheep meat that can be exported to the EEC every year. Finally some measure of free trade in sheep meat is allowable subject to the repayment of any variable premium paid out on the carcases to be exported.

The market place for lamb

The UK sheep industry has been undergoing several changes in recent years which the sheep meat regime has tended to accelerate. The supply of sheep meat in the UK is summarised in Table 11 and highlights both encouraging and discouraging trends (MLC, 1986d). On the positive side the home production of lamb is increasing and more of this production is being both exported and eaten in the UK. At the same time imports are declining and the UK is currently 62% self sufficient in lamb. It is interesting to compare this with the situation in the early 70s when production was low, imports high and only 42% self sufficiency was achieved.

Table 11. Changes in the sheepmeat market 1970–1987 (000t)

	1970–75	1985	1986	1987*
Home production	236	300	290	313
Imports	290	157	125	140
Exports	23	49	60	60
Consumption	505	397	370	393

Estimates

On the negative side the consumption of lamb is declining, market prices are weaker and both consumer price and expenditure is falling. The long term prospects for lamb consumption are summarised in Table 12 assuming current trends continue (MLC, 1986e). The particular features of the current marketing situation which are of concern are the consumer's perception of lamb as being

Table 12. Mutton and lamb consumption projections 1985–1995

	1985	1990	1995	% Change 1995/85
	000 tonnes cwe			
Production	300	320	330	+10
Consumption	397	390	380	−4
of which:				
household consumption:				
fresh	316	309	300	−5
processed	22	23	24	+9
catering consumption:				
fresh	55	54	52	−5
processed	4	4	4	—

fatty, wasteful and difficult to handle combined with the rising age profile of lamb purchasers. The need to produce lean lamb and to present it in a style that matches modern lifestyles is a crucial factor in reversing these predictions and increasing the demand for lamb. If there is to be an increase in consumption then lamb must be seen to be good value. Any increase in retail prices due to a limitation of the variable premium would affect the quantity of lamb purchased.

The current state of the exchange rate of the pound with the French franc has made exporting a relatively attractive proposition in recent months. If this trend continues, as predicted, then there is scope to increase the level of exports in the near future. In the longer term the markets in the whole of the EEC, particularly the newly acceded countries, should be able to absorb up to 80,000 t of British lamb by the end of the decade. However other major sheepmeat exporters are looking to the same markets and the current discrepancies between VRA levels and actual imports to the EEC allow expansion in this area.

Future flock profitability

Combining the likely changes in production costs with the factors highlighted above in relation to the sheepmeat regime gross margins for 1986 and 1987 can be estimated. A summary of estimated gross margins is shown in Table 13. The higher ewe premium payment in 1986 will increase gross margins despite higher feed costs due to the harsh winter. Despite lower cost estimates in 1987 a lower ewe premium will reduce margins to below their likely 1986 level. If the effects of inflation are taken into account then 1987 margins will be below those of 1985 in real terms.

The longer term outlook for lamb prices is for little or no increases with the future level of ewe premium payments uncertain. The current level of concentrate and fertiliser prices cannot be sustained indefinitely and it seems inevitable that there will be a squeeze on sheep margins in the long term. However, in relation to other commodities, the prospects for continuing profitable sheep production are good for the efficient producer.

Table 13. Projected gross margins for 1986 and 1987 compared to 1985 results (£/ewe)

	1985	1986	1987
Lowland	31.06	33.30	32.97
Upland	34.53	38.15	37.24
Hill	29.56	31.25	29.85

REFERENCES

CROSTON, D. and POLLOTT, G. E. (1985) *Planned Sheep Production*. London, UK: Collins.

MLC. (1985) *Sheep Yearbook*. Milton Keynes, UK: MLC.

MLC. (1986a) *Data Sheet 86/1*. Milton Keynes, UK: MLC.

MLC. (1986b) *Data Sheet 86/2*. Milton Keynes, UK: MLC.

MLC. (1986c) *Sheep Yearbook*. Milton Keynes, UK: MLC.

MLC. (1986d) *UK Market Review, 1986/2*. Milton Keynes, UK: MLC.

MLC. (1986e) *Meat Demand Trends, 86/3*. Milton Keynes, UK: MLC.

NEWTON, J. E. and DAVIES, D. A. (1987) White clove and sheep production. In: Pollott, G. E. (ed.) *Efficient Sheep Production from Grass. British Grassland Society, Occasional Publication, No. 21*. pp. 79–87.

Grass Production for Sheep

J. JOHNSON[1] and
B. EVANS[2]
[1]ADAS, Block 2,
Government Buildings,
Lawnswood,
Leeds LS16 5PY
[2]ADAS, Government
Buildings, Penrallt,
Caernarfon LL55 1EP

ABSTRACT

The production of grass to meet the needs of the sheep flock is discussed against a background of an increasing national sheep flock carried on a diminishing area of grassland, and being only partially offset by reduced cattle numbers. Critical periods of the year when increased nutritional demands occur are highlighted. An increased ratio of sheep to cattle on many farms has exaggerated the problems of supplying adequate grazing conditions during the winter and spring.

Survey data on nitrogen fertiliser use emphasises the smaller role this element plays on sheep and beef farms in contrast to dairy farms. It remains a significant factor in determining the output of sheep meat, especially in lowland sheep systems, where nitrogen fertiliser and soil moisture status are major determinants of grass production. On upland farms the shorter growing season, with greater soil and climatic limitations to grass output, represents a further constraint to meeting seasonal nutritional requirements.

The selection of seed mixtures for sheep pastures is considered in relation to lowland and upland situations and the relative performance of permanent pastures with sown leys. The role of earlier growing grasses and of grass/clover variety selections which might improve utilisation of the potential nutritional and nitrogen supplying benefits of the legumes are discussed.

Data from commercial farms demonstrate deficiencies in current practices resulting in overgrazing in spring and undergrazing later in the season. Management practices which might be adopted to alleviate such deficiencies are discussed, including the timing of nitrogen fertiliser, winter resting of sheep pastures, the use of supplementary feeding and a more flexible integration of grazing with silage cutting, to achieve an improved balance between grass supply and sheep requirements.

INTRODUCTION

The area of grassland in UK, particularly that under five years old, continues to decline (MAFF, 1986). At the same time there has been a 30% increase in the national sheep flock, which now exceeds 37 million, since 1975. This increase in numbers has generally been faster in the lowlands (Slade, ADAS, personal communication).

Table 1. Area of grassland in UK 1984–1986 ('000 hectares)

	1984	1985	1986
Grass below five years old	1794	1796	1718
Grass more than five years old	5105	5019	5080
Rough grazing (sole right)	4895	4872	4857

MAFF (1986)

The reduction in grassland area and the increase in sheep numbers have only been partially offset by reduced cattle numbers. The overall effect is of increased pressure on the grassland area, since historically there is little evidence of a high use of grain and other concentrates to supplement the energy requirements of sheep (Green and Baker, 1981).

Table 2. Contribution of grain and other concentrated feeds to the energy requirements of different classes of stock (%)

Livestock	1951	1961	1971	1976
Dairy	21	29	33	40
Beef	16	19	20	21
Sheep and horses	7	4	6	3
All classes	16	19	22	24

The increased ratio of sheep : cattle, independently of overall stocking rate, also has an impact on the ability of grassland to meet the nutritional needs of the sheep flock. The higher proportional dependence of sheep to meet their energy needs from forage, relative to cattle, has already been demonstrated. Perhaps of more importance is the longer period of housing when feed requirements are supplied by conserved forages, with or without supplementation, associated with cattle production systems. Thus the increase in sheep numbers places much greater pressure on grazing land during winter and spring when herbage supply rates are at a minimum. Conversely the lower use of conserved forage where sheep replace cattle, reduces the role that conservation can play in controlling grazing pressure during the periods of high herbage growth rates in early summer. This change therefore increases the potential for over-grazing during the winter and spring and undergrazing in summer.

Seasonal changes reflecting the various physiological states of the ewe can be estimated in terms of daily metabolisable energy (ME) requirement (ARC, 1980). Requirements for other ewe types vary according to live weight, growth of young ewes and lambing rate. It has also been noted (Milne, 1985) that nutrient needs at different times of the production cycle are not independent of one another and our ability to predict nutrient supply from pasture or from a combination of pasture and supplements remains suspect with many gaps in our knowledge.

Table 3. Metabolisable energy requirement of a mature 70 kg ewe producing twins

	MJ per day
Dry period	9.0
Flushing	15.0
Early pregnancy	15.0
Mid-late pregnancy	9.5–19.0
Early lactation	22.5
Mid-late lactation	22.5–9.0

HERBAGE PRODUCTION

The total amount of herbage produced from grassland is dependent on a range of independent environmental factors in addition to those such as sward type and fertiliser use under control of the farmer. On lowland swards total production is principally a function of soil type and moisture status (Morrison et al., 1980). Sites with lower productive potential are characterised by low growth rates under moisture stress during the mid-summer (Figure 1). Potential yield in average years can be estimated (Table 4) according to grass growth class (ADAS, 1987).

The guidelines derived from trials on soils of generally low to moderate fertility bear little relationship to current fertiliser use on sheep production systems (see below). In practice when nitrogen use on grassland has exceeded 250 kg/ha for a number of years a buildup of soil nitrogen should allow for a cut back on late season applications, and in general applications of fertiliser nitrogen during drought and after mid-August are not justified.

On upland and hill swards other factors become of greater importance. On six upland sites (>200 m) in which perennial ryegrass was less than 30% of the species present, Hopkins et al. (1986b) found production levels to be 30% below those obtained at lowland sites. A further limiting characteristic of upland pastures is the short growing season. On an improved pasture at 350 m in mid-Wales receiving 60 kg/ha N in April and grazed by sheep and cattle 75% of the total herbage production measured under exclusion cages was obtained between late May and mid August (Evans, unpublished data). The implications of this variability in levels and patterns of herbage production will be discussed in relation to management strategies for various sheep systems.

MANURING

Despite the widely recognised knowledge that fertiliser nitrogen can be used both safely and effectively and applied during grazing (Cunningham, 1984) the overall use of nitrogen on beef and sheep farms falls well below that of dairy farms, whether the grass is used for grazing, hay or silage (Archer, 1986).

15

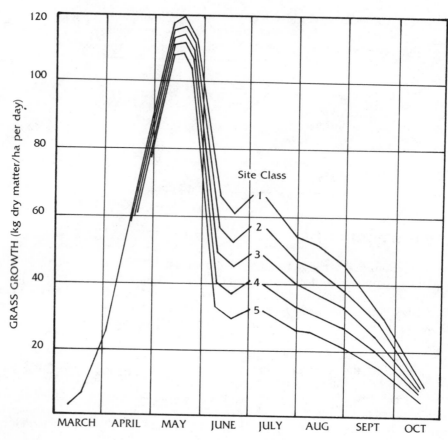

Figure 1. The effect of site class on grass growth.

Table 4. Potential yield and optimum annual fertiliser nitrogen

Grass growth class	Potential yield (t/ha)	Optimum annual fertiliser nitrogen (kg/ha)
Poor	8.4	300
Fair	9.5	330
Average	10.5	370
Good	11.6	410
Very good	12.7	450

Table 5. Average overall use of nitrogen on grass for different farm types in England and Wales (kg N/ha).

	Dairying		Beef and sheep	
	1974	1984	1974	1984
Grazed only	80	122	49	57
Cut for hay	79	94	50	71
Cut for silage	194	221	164	181
All grass	96	147	54	79

The higher proportion of white clover found on beef and sheep farms compared with dairy farms (Forbes *et al.*, 1980) may go some way to replace fertiliser nitrogen but would do little to assist in the need for herbage in spring and late summer when clover growth relative to grass growth is slow.

Amongst MLC recorded flocks nitrogen use was 154 kg/ha on average with the top third averaging 208 kg/ha (MLC, 1985), with nitrogen use of 166 kg/ha on lowland sheep systems and only 104 kg/ha on upland systems. Live weight stocked per kg of nitrogen used on upland farms was 7.89 kg and 6.97 kg for lowland farms, indicating a more efficient fertiliser nitrogen use in upland areas.

There was a close relationship between nitrogen use and liveweight per hectare, ewe weight per hectare and lamb weight produced per hectare (Table 6). One half of the sample used below 150 kg/ha of nitrogen.

Table 6. Grassland productivity at different levels of nitrogen use

Nitrogen use kg/ha	% of farms	Liveweight per hectare (kg)	Ewe weight per hectare (kg)	Lamb weight per hectare (kg)
1– 50	9	709	559	397
51–100	20	895	723	503
101–150	21	1075	802	580
151–200	24	1129	874	655
201–250	14	1272	960	748
251–300	8	1378	1069	804
300+	4	1630	1161	875

MLC (1985)

LIME, PHOSPHATE AND POTASH

For sheep grazing, especially where a high clover level is to be encouraged, the importance of satisfactory levels of lime, phosphate and potash cannot be over-emphasised. Lime is essential, especially for hill pastures, where there is an increased reliance on white clover. Both white clover and its rhizobia operate at their best between pH 5.5 and 6.0 (Frame, Newbould and Munro, 1985). The slow movement of lime down the profile of a surface improved peat soil has been highlighted (Davies, 1984) and indicates that much lower levels of 2.5–5.0 t per hectare of ground limestone may be an adequate first dressing (Frame, Newbould and Munro, 1985).

A dressing of 120 kg/ha P_2O_5 every 4–6 years and 20–40 kg/ha K_2O (more on deeper peats) is suggested as adequate on upland improved pastures (Davies, 1984) with the overall aim of maintaining phosphate and potash at indices of 2 and 1 respectively. A complete fertiliser applied annually is an alternative approach. In practice farmers would be well advised to have improved land checked for these basic elements on a regular basis if a worthwhile response to the limited amount of fertiliser nitrogen is to be achieved and if white clover is to fulfil a prominent role.

VARIETIES AND SEED MIXTURES, SWARD TYPES

A recent assessment (MLC, 1985) of grassland areas categorised as having more than 80% of their area as leys or permanent pasture suggested that permanent pasture appears to be less productive than leys. The role of white clover in terms of both enhanced nutritive value and saving of fertiliser nitrogen has been widely considered (Thomson, 1984; Frame and Newbould, 1984).

Table 7. Grassland productivity from leys and permanent pasture at different levels of nitrogen use (kg of liveweight/ha).

Nitrogen use (kg/ha)	Leys*	Permanent pasture*
51–100	1173	929
101–150	1191	1013
151–200	1135	1064
201–250	1447	1274
251–300	1426	1412

Lowland and upland farms with more than 80% of their grassland falling into this category

The apparent difference in animal output between leys and permanent pasture is unlikely to be explained by large differences in dry matter yield between the two sward types. Hopkins *et al.* (1986a) demonstrated the high yield superiority of reseeded grass in its first full year compared with permanent pasture. In 1985, the second full year of the reseed, the yield advantage of the reseeds was reduced or eliminated, and only at levels of nitrogen at 450 kg/ha and above did reseeds yield consistently higher, by around 10%. Certainly in this trial when the yield loss in the reseeding phase is credited to the permanent pasture there appears little benefit in total yield terms over the two years of the trial.

Table 8. Annual dry matter yields (t/ha) from permanent and reseeded swards under four weekly cutting. (Mean of 16 sites, 1984.)

	Fertiliser N (kg/ha)				
	0	150	300	450	900
Permanent pasture	3.73	6.25	8.17	9.73	9.76
Perennial ryegrass reseed	5.30	8.77	11.74	13.22	14.26

Whilst absolute yield may be an important consideration, especially for conservation, small differences between species and cultivars due to such factors as earliness of spring growth, enhanced nutritive value, ease of grazing can result in differences in animal production potential.

Advice on varieties and mixtures is embodied in ADAS P2041 (ADAS, 1986a) and mixtures are suggested to cover a range of durations and management systems. The selection of varieties for lowland systems in arable rotations will be different from a mixture for hills and uplands. For example at Rosemaund EHF in Hereford the five year ley mixture for sheep is based on diploid and tetraploid perennial ryegrass and a large leaved white clover. At Redesdale EFH in Northumberland the mixture is based on late heading diploid and tetraploid ryegrasses, Timothy and small leaved white clover.

On wet hill soils grasses such as red fescue and Timothy can give better lamb production than perennial ryegrass (Davies and Evans, 1986) and at the other extreme for short term leys hybrid ryegrass has given higher feed intake and liveweight gain than Italian and is also more persistent.

Progress with perennial ryegrass varieties, especially tetraploids, has been great in recent years (Aldrich, 1986) and evidence from Redesdale EHF (ADAS, unpublished) indicates that they can persist almost as well as diploids under their conditions. Kent wild white clover has been superior to N. Zealand Huia in these studies.

Davies and Evans (1986) have demonstrated over six years a yield of 1.2 t DM/ha from the early ryegrass Frances compared to 0.8 and 0.6 t DM/ha from Talbot (medium) and Melle (late) types at Pant-y-dwr. Although in the past

Table 9. Ground cover % of two cultivars of white clover when grown with diploid or tetraploid ryegrass

| | Kent Wild White | | NZ Huia | |
	Ryegrass	Clover	Ryegrass	Clover
Diploid† ryegrass	43	19	53	6
Tetraploid* ryegrass	39	25	46	5

†*Mean of cultivars Contender, Lamora, Mascot, Melle, Parcour, Perma, Trani*
Mean of cultivars Belfort, Condesa, Meltra

earliness of spring growth has been associated with reduced persistency such varieties and newer varieties such as Liprior may have an increasing role provided management prevents excessive heading in mid-season.

Recent work at Bronydd Mawr (Munro, personal communication) compared three ryegrass varieties (Aurora, Meltra and S23) for spring lamb production under upland conditions and demonstrated the potential of the early ryegrass Aurora. Also this variety has tended to blend well with white clover. It may be that this variety has a place, along with others, for the provision of early grass in spring.

Table 10. Spring lamb production (kg/ha) late April–early June

	Aurora	Meltra	S23
1985	213	157	129
1986	338	271	233
Mean	276	215	181

In a further study to assess the effect of white clover on total dry matter yield, the smaller leaved cultivars proved superior to the medium leaved (Redesdale EHF).

Table 11. Response (kg/ha) for inclusion of white clover with Perma perennial ryegrass receiving 100 kg/ha N annually. (Mean 1980–1985)

	Perma + clover	Perma alone	Benefit from clover	% Clover contribution
All varieties*	8517	6368	2149	34
S184 + Kent	8830	6368	2462	39

Mean of Huia, S100, Donna, Menna, Sonja, S184, Pronitro, Kent

INCREASING HERBAGE AVAILABILITY

Timing of fertiliser nitrogen in spring

Extensive trials have been undertaken on this subject by ADAS in England and Wales (Archer and Unwin, 1984) and Scotland (Swift *et al.*, 1985). ADAS results, for example, showed that on 80% of sites there was a period of at least 20 days over which fertiliser could be applied to obtain 90% of maximum yield and that although the accumulated mean daily air temperature usually reached T °200C within that period this was not a critical value.

ADAS advice currently (ADAS, 1987) is that on soils where early grazing is possible, nitrogen can be applied from early to mid-February at lowland sites in Wales and the south of England when soil conditions permit. Progressively later dates between late-February to mid-March are a guide in eastern and northern districts.

On upland sites the T 200 sum has been found to be too early in studies in Scotland (Harkness and Frame, 1985). Davies (1985) found a response to 45 kg/ha N applied on 1 April of over 5 kg DM per kgN in only 8 of 18 years on a poorly drained upland site. There was poor correlation to T °200 but there was a correlation to soil temperature at 100 mm depth.

Starr (ADAS, personal communication) showed a significant effect of site aspect on the date at which T °200 was reached. At a similar altitude and location there was a three-week difference between a favoured southerly aspect and disadvantaged northerly aspect.

In trials in Wales (ADAS, 1984a) nitrogen timing of at 60 kg/ha on 10–15 March or 5–10 April was compared on two upland sites (275–300 masl) to swards rested from January or from March. Nitrogen applied at the earlier date always produced similar or additional herbage mass during late April and early May. The benefit of the earlier application occurred more frequently on pasture rested during the January–March period. Site differences were also apparent in this study where the response to earlier nitrogen was better at the lower altitude (275 v 305 m) and with less exposed aspect despite this site being on permanent grass of lower perennial ryegrass content (20%) than the higher site (60% perennial ryegrass).

Table 12. Effect of date of N application on herbage mass (kg DM/ha) in early May on pastures rested from January or March

	60 kg/ha N applied	
	March	April
Rested from January	1730	1457
Grazed to 20 March	1173	1147
Mean	1452	1302

There is therefore considerable safety in applying nitrogen fertiliser on well drained soils, even at altitudes of 300 m, as early as mid-March, and at least on some sites and seasons, significant benefits in the supply of grazing during April are obtainable. It is notable that the increase in herbage mass resulting from early nitrogen application represented an increase in green leaf mass, that part of the sward available as high quality nutrient to the grazing ewe.

In practice there is still a reluctance, especially on upland farms, to apply nitrogen even for early grazing despite the large yield and quality responses and the achievement of optimum sward height at an early stage.

This response can be converted into heavier lambs at three weeks, heavier male lambs for sale in autumn, and heavier ewe lamb weights which could have implications on mature ewe weight.

Table 13. Herbage production and quality on swards with and without fertiliser nitrogen

	Nitrogen*	
	−	+
Yield (t DM/ha)	1.20	2.35
ME (MJ/kg DM)	11.8	12.2
DCP (g/kg DM)	137	201

*90 kg/ha applied on 12 March. Harvested 2 May

More recent work has demonstrated the benefit of spring nitrogen on intensively winter grazed upland pasture in terms of heavier stocking rates, reduced cake inputs and a higher proportion of heavier lambs at first draw. The overall direct benefit from a single application of fertiliser nitrogen was almost 2½ times the cost of fertiliser.

Earlier application of fertiliser nitrogen could also contribute to earlier spring grazing, its cost being offset, and in some cases eliminated, by less use of nitrogen in May and June, when grass is frequently under-utilised. This change in the pattern of nitrogen application should also contribute to an improvement in the clover content of grazed pasture, a change which would also be favoured by achieving a more uniform grazing height during the early summer.

Form of fertiliser nitrogen

It appears that 70–90% of nitrogen is taken up by plants in the form of ammonium at 3–10°C when ammonium and nitrate forms are present in equal amounts (in flowing solution, Jones *et al.*, 1982). Benefits can be achieved by using only the

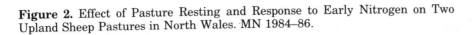

Figure 2. Effect of Pasture Resting and Response to Early Nitrogen on Two Upland Sheep Pastures in North Wales. MN 1984–86.

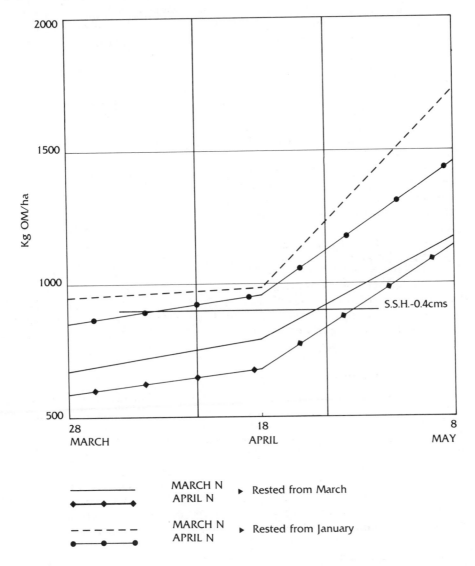

ammonium form of nitrogen due to lower leaching losses and higher yields (Baker, 1986). Work by ADAS (Chumbley, 1986) found no difference between ammonium nitrate, calcium nitrate and ammonium sulphate. The practical significance of a change in the form of fertiliser nitrogen both for spring and late summer application merits further study.

Minimising winter grazing effects

Mention has already been made of the role of spring nitrogen to increased spring herbage production. In addition the practice of resting pasture by adopting housing, limiting the grazing area or grazing stubbles, whilst feasible, can create management problems (Cunningham, 1984). Winter resting can double herbage availability in spring and when associated with an early application of nitrogen a four fold increase in grass available in spring can be achieved (Taylor and Cowdy, 1985).

Agistment of sheep, especially ewe hoggs, from upland to lowland from late autumn into winter has been traditional practice benefiting the hill farmer by:
– producing better store and finished lambs
– increasing size of ewe hoggs which has a major effect on long term prolificacy (ADAS, 1986b)
– a reduced grazing pressure at home increasing ewe lambing %
– increased herbage available in spring
– larger ewe lambs
and the lowland farmer benefiting by:
– reduced winter-kill
– reduced wastage and poaching
– production of highly tillered swards, especially new reseeds.

The ADAS program "Winter Grass" helps to put farmers wishing to send away sheep and those wishing to receive them.

Recent work at Liscombe (ADAS, unpublished) has shown that for each week grazing after the end of March until the beginning of May there was a 6% reduction in both first cut and total yield. Increased nitrogen use could not compensate for late grazing.

Pasture management in late summer

Pasture condition in late summer has been shown to be improved by maintaining pastures below 6 cm in the early and mid season. Observations on four upland pastures during October–November 1984 (ADAS, 1984b) indicated that sward quality can be a particular problem both nutritionally and for longer term sward survival when grass is conserved *in situ* for use during this period. On pastures which were rested during September following nitrogen application in late August sward height increased to around 20 cm by early October. When grazed down to 7 cm by late November only 25% of the available herbage consisted of green leaf. Swards grazed during September with a sward surface height of 10–11 cm by early October contained 35–52% green leaf in late November when grazing height was 4–4.5 cm.

Based on research and development studies Parsons (1984) has proposed a profile of sward height as a guideline to the management of a lowland sheep system. Under upland and hill conditions the requirement is for a spring application of 50–60 kg/ha N to promote spring growth from, for example, perennial ryegrass, reliance on white clover during the summer months and perhaps a second dressing of fertiliser nitrogen (in a compound to replace phosphate and potash) to produce sufficient herbage mass for a long flushing and tupping period from mid October (Wilkinson, 1985).

Table 14. Yield (kg DM/ha) and yield response (DM/kg N) from a late summer application of 50 kg/ha N

	N applied on				
	Control	27 July	10 August	24 August	7 September
Yield on 22 October	1630	2319	2085	2077	1981
kg DM/kg N	—	14	9	9	7

Redesdale EHF

Work at Redesdale EHF (Merrell, personal communication) has examined the dry matter yield response from a late summer application of nitrogen (Table 14). In each of three years a worthwhile response was achieved at all nitrogen timings with a variable effect on white clover, being reduced, but not in all years.

More recent work (ADAS, unpublished) on a number of sites in Wales confirmed the relatively high levels of response to late summer application of nitrogen (20.0 to 10.0 kg DM/kg N) depending on timing, of swards which had received minimal amounts of fertiliser nitrogen during the season.

SYSTEMS STUDIES

Use of sward surface height in sheep production systems

The successful integration of components of research into farming systems has been an important feature of development and advisory approaches. In a study on upland sheep farms in North Wales Barron (1984) monitored sward surface heights on six fields grazed continuously by ewes and lambs during the period April to July.

Table 15. Sward surface height on six continuously grazed sheep pastures on upland farms in North Wales April–July 1984

Date	No. fields <4 cm	No. fields >6 cm	Min.–max. range cm
18 April	5	1	2.8– 5.0
2 May	0	1	4.0– 7.4
16 May	1	1	3.2– 6.5
30 May	0	3	4.6– 7.5
13 June	0	5	4.7–16.8
27 June	1	5	3.9–20.1
11 July	1	4	3.9–25.2

These results are considered typical of this predominantly sheep/livestock rearing upland area, and showed that ewes and lambs were grazing pastures generally lower than 4 cm in mid-April. In contrast most fields were being undergrazed by early June with four of the six fields surveyed becoming undergrazed with extensive areas of rejection and stem formation by mid-June. A notable feature of the management of these fields was the timing of nitrogen fertiliser application. Four out of six fields received nitrogen between 7 and 16 April, the remaining two on 20 May. All the fields received a second dressing in late May and June when undergrazing was already apparent on at least four of the fields.

ADAS (1985) monitored sward surface height in four fields on a Brecon farm carrying a late February/March lambing flock during late April–late June 1985. Sward height also exceeded 6 cm by early June on all fields reaching 9.3–15.5 cm by late June. This increase was associated with the sale of lambs during May and June and a consequent reduction in liveweight carried per hectare.

These results clearly demonstrate the potential for improved utilisation of pasture during the lamb rearing period in current commercial sheep systems. A greater degree of stocking rate control brought about by a greater flexibility to close off fields for silage could improve output from the grazed area and supply additional forage for winter feeding. This additional conserved material could contribute to a greater ability to rest pastures during the late winter (used as a supplement to a reduced late winter grazing area or by housing) and alleviate the lack of grazing at lambing time.

The Liscombe System

An integrated cutting and grazing system for Liscombe EHF has recently been described (Appleton, 1985):

Early March – 60 kg/ha nitrogen applied. Sheep grazing at 7.5 ewes per hectare.

Late spring – one third of grass area shut up for silage receives 100 kg/ha N plus P and K.
– one third grazed at 18 ewes/ha with twins.
– one third grazed at 25 ewes/ha with singles.
– 60 kg/ha N applied to grazing area.

Summer – dry ewes graze at 45/ha.
– weaned lambs graze at 50/ha.
– 60 kg/ha N applied in early June.
– about one third of area shut up for silage receives 100 kg/ha N plus P and K.

Late Summer – fat ewes stocked at 25/ha.
– thin ewes stocked at 18/ha.
– 60 kg/ha N applied in late August.

Autumn – tupping at 15 ewes/ha.

Total nitrogen use – 240 kg/ha N for grazing
– 260 kg/ha N for grazing/cutting.

This system produces an output of 700 kg of lamb gain per hectare plus four tonnes of silage per ewe for winter feeding and lamb finishing.

A system less reliant on fertiliser nitrogen is practised at Rosemaund EHF (D. Brown, personal communication) where nitrogen use of around 125 kg/ha in total is restricted to early spring, mid- and late summer on ryegrass/white clover on long leys in arable rotations. Such a manuring system is appropriate to both lowland and upland systems for grass/clover swards (ADAS, 1987).

Grass height as a system control

It is important that the recent increased understanding of herbage production and utilisation is integrated into farming systems. Maxwell *et al.* (1985) described various systems experiments in which sward height was used to control grazing management. Integral features of these studies have been the use of conservation areas to adjust stocking rates in order to maintain target grazing height. This approach demands a move away from the current practice of having inflexibility in the cutting area, date of cutting and stocking rate on the grazing area. Only 20–30% of the conservation area needs managing with greater flexibility regarding fencing and duration of the crop. Problems of conserving this small area could be overcome using baled silage independent of the main silage crop.

Management guidelines based on research and systems studies for lowland and upland sheep are summarised later by Maxwell and Treacher (1987). Development studies are currently in progress on EHFs in which systems using sward height as a controlling mechanism are being compared with current management practices. These guidelines are also being incorporated into a grassland planning system for advisory use by ADAS.

REFERENCES

ADAS, Trawsgoed, Dyfed SY23 4HT. (1984a) Winter management of upland sheep pastures. *Agronomy, Wales. Results of Experiments 1984/6* (in press).

ADAS, Trawsgoed, Dyfed SY23 4HT. (1984b) Availability of herbage on upland pasture grazed by sheep during the ewe breeding season. *Agronomy, Wales. Results of Experiments 1984.*

ADAS, Trawsgoed, Dyfed SY23 4HT. (1985) Monitoring of sward height and herbage mass under normal farm practice. *Agronomy, Wales. Results of Experiments 1985.*

ADAS Publications, Alnwick, Northumberland. (1986a) *Grass Seed Mixtures P2041.*

ADAS Publications, Alnwick, Northumberland. (1986b) *N. Region Livestock Notes 86/11.*

ADAS Publications, Alnwick, Northumberland. (1987) *Fertiliser Recommendations* (in press).

ALDRICH, D. T. A. (1986) A review of the last four years. Paper presented at *NIAB Fellows' Conference, Hampshire,* January 1986.

APPLETON, M. (1985) Advances in sheep grazing systems. In: Frame, J. (ed.) *Grazing. British Grassland Society Occasional Symposium No. 19,* pp. 167–174.

ARC. (1980) *The Nutritional Requirements of Ruminant Livestock.* Slough, UK: CAB.

ARCHER, F. C. and UNWIN, R. J. (1984) The timing of first nitrogen application to maximise the yield of early grass. *Proceedings 10th European Grassland Federation, Norway.*

ARCHER, J. R. (1986) Grassland manuring past and present. In: Cooper, J. P. and Raymond, W. F. (eds) Grassland Manuring. British Grassland Occasional Symposium No. 20, pp. 5–14.

BAKER, R. D. (1986) Efficient use of nitrogen fertilisers. In: Cooper, J. P. and Raymond, W. F. (eds) *Grassland Manuring. British Grassland Occasional Symposium No. 20,* pp. 15–27.

BARRON, J. D. ADAS Trawsgoed, Dyfed SY23 4HT. (1984) *ADAS Training Project Report.*

CHUMBLEY, C. G. (1986) Forms of nitrogen for early grass production. In: Cooper, J. P. and Raymond, W. F. (eds) *Grassland Manuring. British Grassland Occasional Symposium No. 20*, pp. 32–85.

CUNNINGHAM, J. M. M. (1984) The use of grass in sheep production. In: Corrall, A. J. (ed.) *Money from grass, Occasional Symposium No. 15, British Grassland Society*, pp. 34–47.

DAVIES, A. and EVANS, WILL (1986) The role of improved grass and clover varieties in lamb production. In: *Science and Quality Lamb Production*. (ed.) J. Hardcastle, pp. 18–20 AFRC.

DAVIES, D. A. (1985) Improving spring growth. *Proceedings of the Second Welsh Agricultural Research and Development Conference Bangor*, p. 21.

DAVIES, M. H. MAFF Publications, Alnwick, Northumberland. (1984) *Redesdale Annual Review*, p. 28.

FORBES, T. J., DIBB, C., GREEN, J. O., HOPKINS, A. and PEEL, S. (1980) *Factors Affecting the Productivity of Permanent Grassland ADAS/GRI Joint Permanent Pasture Group*. A National Farm Study.

FRAME, J. and NEWBOULD, P. (1984) Herbage production for grass/white clover swards. *BGS Occ. Symp. No. 16*. (ed.) D. J. Thomson, p. 15–35.

FRAME, J., NEWBOULD, P. and MUNRO, J. M. M. (1985) Herbage production from the hills and upland. In: Maxwell, T. J. and Gunn, R. G. (eds) *Hill and Upland Livestock Production, British Society of Animal Production Occasional Publication No. 10*, pp. 9–37.

GREEN, J. O. and BAKER, R. D. (1981) Classification, distribution and productivity of UK grasslands. In: Jollons, J. L. (ed.) *Grassland in the British Economy. CAB Paper 10*, pp. 237–247 Reading, Centre for Agriculture Strategy.

HARKNESS, R. D. and FRAME, J. (1985) Efficiency of nitrogen application rate and timing on grass swards (in press).

HOPKINS, A., DIBB, C., GILBEY, J., MURRAY, P. J., BOWLING, P. J. and WILSON, I. A. N. (1986) Production and response to nitrogen of permanent and reseeded grassland. In: Cooper, J. P. and Raymond, W. F. (eds) *Grassland Manuring. British Grassland Occasional Symposium No. 20*, pp. 79–81.

HOPKINS, A., GILBEY, J. and DIBB, C. (1986) The response of upland permanent pasture to fertiliser nitrogen. In: O'Toole, M. A. (ed.) *Hill Land Symposium*, 64–77. Dublin, Eire: An Foras Taluntais.

JONES, L. H. P., HOPPER, M. J., HATCH, D. J. and CLARKSON, D. T. (1982) Uptake of ions from solutions of controlled composition. *Grassland Research Institute, Annual Report. 1981*, pp. 19–20.

MAFF Whitehall Place London SW1A 2HH. (1986) Press Release, No. 224. August 21, 1986.

MAXWELL, T. J., LLOYD, MARY D. and DICKSON, I. A. (1985) Upland sheep production systems. In: Maxwell, T. J. and Gunn, R. G. (eds). *Hill and Upland Livestock Production, British Society of Animal Production Occasional Publication No. 10*, pp. 96–106.

MLC. (1985) *Sheep Yearbook*. Milton Keynes, UK; MLC.

MILNE, J. A. (1985) Nutritional needs of sheep in the hills and uplands. In: Maxwell, T. J. and Gunn, R. G. (eds.) *Hill and Upland Livestock Production, British Society of Animal Production Occasional Publication No. 10*, pp. 39–48.

MORRISON, J., JACKSON, M. V. and SPARROW, P. E. (1980) The response of perennial ryegrass to fertiliser nitrogen in relation to climate and soil. *Grassland Research Institute Technical Report No. 27*.

PARSONS, A. J. (1984) Guidelines for management of continuously grazed swards. *Grass Farmer BGS Spring 1984*.

SWIFT, G., MACKIE, C. K., HARKNESS, R. D. and FRANKLIN, M. F. (1985) Timing of nitrogen for spring grass. *The Scottish Agricultural College's Research Note No. 10*.

TAYLOR, T. and COWDY, P. (1985) Spring grass from sheep housing. *Agricultural R and D in Wales, Second Conf., Bangor, April 1985*, p. 36.

THOMSON, D. J. (1984) The nutritive value of white clover. In: Thomson, D. J. (ed.) *Forage Legumes, Occasional Symposium No. 16, British Grassland Society*, pp. 78–92.

WILKINSON, M. MAFF Publications, Alnwick, Northumberland. (1985) *Redesdale EHF Annual Review, 1985*.

Grass as a Feed for Sheep
– its Potential and Limitations

A. W. SPEEDY and
DAWN BAZELY
University of Oxford,
Agricultural Science
Building, Parks Road,
Oxford OX1 3PF

ABSTRACT

Factors affecting grass consumption, the nutritive value of herbage, energy and protein utilisation and lamb production from grass are reviewed. Herbage production, herbage intake, digestion and metabolism, milk production, ewe body weight change and lamb growth are considered as components of an integrated model of the grazing system. A simulation model is used to demonstrate the effects of supplementary feeding and grazing limitations on the ewe and lamb.

INTRODUCTION

Consideration of the theoretical potential and limitations of grazed pasture requires an understanding of a complex model involving soil/plant/animal/ management interactions. Variation exists in herbage growth and the seasonal pattern of available herbage, in the nutritive value of grass, in animal intake, nutrient requirements and animal production. The aim of understanding the components of this model is to produce a working simulation of lamb production from grass and to achieve a more objective basis for grassland management.

HERBAGE PRODUCTION

Grass production depends on soil conditions, temperature and rainfall and varies considerably between sites and between years. Annual dry matter yield of grass at Wytham, Oxford ranged from 9.3–12.7 t/ha at 300 kg N/ha and showed an average response (0–300 kg N/ha) of 25 kg DM/kg N (Morrison *et al.*, 1980). In this study (GM20), there was considerable variation between sites in both yield and nitrogen response. At the same level of nitrogen, mean yield at Hurley was 7.9 t/ha compared to 11.3 t/ha in Devon. There were correlations between both maximum and optimum yields and rainfall during the growing season and available water holding capacity of the soil.

An annual production of 10,000 kg DM/ha provides a theoretical capability to support 14 ewes with 21 lambs per ha (at 700/kg DM/ewe-lamb unit). The problem is to synchronise the seasonal pattern of dry-matter production with the pattern of animal requirements.

The seasonal pattern of herbage production from simulated grazing (cutting) experiments shows the classical bi-modal peaks (Figure 1). An equation of the following type may be fitted to the data from different sites:

Daily DM yield = $A(SIN((X-B)/C) \times 360) \times (1-D) (SIN((X-E)/F) \times 360)$

The coefficients can be related to the timing of the growing season, rainfall and soil moisture holding characteristics. The equation fitted to the data from Wytham is:

DMy = $230 (SIN((X-75/420) \times 360) \times (1-0.7) (SIN((X-105)/365) \times 360)$

However, recent evidence suggests that, under continuous grazing, the herbage production curve has a single mid-summer peak, which contrasts with observations from cut swards (Parsons, 1985; Barthram, 1986) (Figure 1).

THE NUTRITIVE VALUE OF GRASS

There is considerable variation in the nutritional value of grass, arising from differences in species, age, management, location, altitude and season. Even within a perennial ryegrass sward cut throughout the season, there is a wide range in fibre content (MADF), nitrogen, calcium, magnesium, potassium and phosphorus content (Table 1). There may also be important differences in trace element availability, depending on soil levels and management.

In practice, the energy value of pasture is likely to range from 9.5 to 12 MJ ME/kg DM and crude protein from 120 to 220 g/kg DM. These values may be used to predict aniaml performance by the method described by ARC (1980, 1984).

Table 1. The range of composition and nutritive value of perennial ryegrass (from Morrison *et al.*, 1980) cut six times

	Range
MADF[1] (g/kg)	190–300
D value[2]	64–77
Calculated ME (MJ/kg DM)	9.6–11.6
N content[3] (g/kg)	18–42
Calculated CP[4] (g/kg)	113–262
Ca　　　(g/kg)	5.3–9.9
Mg　　　(g/kg)	1.7–3.6
K　　　(g/kg)	2.4–3.5
Na　　　(g/kg)	1.2–4.0
P　　　(g/kg)	3.1–4.3

[1]*Modified Acid Detergent Fibre*
[2]*Digestible organic matter in dry matter*
[3]*At 300 kg fertiliser N/ha*
[4]*N × 6.25*

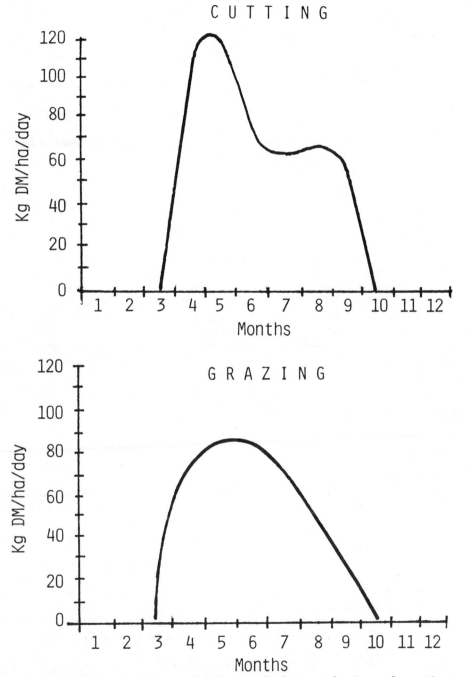

Figure 1. The shapes of the curve of daily gross herbage production under cutting and continuous grazing.

However, differences in energy and protein utilisation due to differences in the rumen degradation of dietary components, products of fermentation, microbial growth yields, accumulation of material in the rumen and the outflow of protein and other materials may have profound effects on predicted voluntary feed consumption and liveweight gain. This may be particularly significant when comparing different types of pasture, especially white clover compared to perennial ryegrass.

For example, the ARC method (ARC, 1984) assumes a microbial protein yield of 32 g N per kg OMADR (organic matter apparently digested in the rumen). Yet Cammell *et al.* (1983) found average values of 53.4 g microbial N/kg OMADR for ryegrass and 66–112 g/kg for white clover.

More complicated models of rumen fermentation based on fundamental aspects of rumen function have been developed to more accurately predict energy and amino acid supply (Beever *et al.*, 1980; Baldwin *et al.*, 1977). Black *et al.* (1982) have used additional data in the simulation of pasture effects on intake and performance of sheep, including structural carbohydrates (hemicellulose, cellulose, lignin), storage carbohydrates (pectin, water soluble polysaccharides), water soluble sugars, true protein, non-protein nitrogen, lipid, ash and inorganic sulphur. In addition, they have taken account of the degradability of structural carbohydrates and protein and animal factors, such as time spent feeding and ruminating. The model is particularly sensitive to protein degradability and rumen outflow rates (Black *et al.*, 1980). The authors note that such full analysis of chemical components, required for this simulation, are not often available.

Black *et al.* (1982) predicted considerable differences between sheep fed *ad libitum* on clover and ryegrass in both intake (1574 g/day v 1298 g/day) and empty body weight gain (174 g/day v 103 g/day).

DRY MATTER INTAKE

A major problem in predicting animal responses at pasture is the assessment of intake which depends on animal factors (size and physiological state) and on nutritive value, herbage mass and physical structure of the sward.

ARC (1980) do not derive specific equations for intake of grass but include grazed herbage under "coarse diets". The equation derived from combining published data was:

$$DMI = 104.7q + 0.307W - 15.0$$

(where q = metabolisability of the diet (ME/GE) and W = live weight).

For a diet where q = 0.6 (11 M/D or 73D), the predicted intake is 54 g/kg $W^{0.75}$ at 20 kg (25.5 g/kg W) and 60 g/kg $W^{0.75}$ at 40 kg (24 g/kg W).

Treacher (unpublished, quoted by Edelsten and Newton, 1975) gave potential intakes of lambs ranging from 21 g/kg at 23 days to 34 g/kg at 84 days, but with a higher intake of milk (42 g/kg) from birth. ARC (1980) quote intakes of 80 g DM/kg $W^{0.75}$ (44 g/kg W) for milk in the first four weeks, declining to 60 g DM/kg $W^{0.75}$ (24 g/kg W).

The intake of dry and pregnant ewes is in the range 60–70 g/kg $W^{0.75}$ (1.45–1.7 kg DM/day for a 70 kg ewe) with a decline occurring sometimes, but not invariably, in late pregnancy (Ferguson, 1974).

Lactating ewes eat 20 to 70 per cent more than comparable dry ewes (according to ARC, 1980), the difference being higher on good diets and for ewes suckling twins. Representative values for intake of pasture herbage are 100 and 110 g/kg $W^{0.75}$ for single- and twin-suckling ewes respectively (ARC, 1980).

The pattern of intake of ewes over the whole production cycle is shown in Figure 2 and is derived from Fourier analysis of daily intakes of a complete diet (Speedy, 1972).

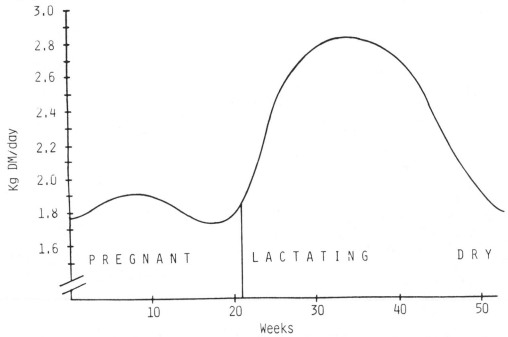

Figure 2. Pattern of dry matter intake of ewes fed a complete diet over the production cycle (Speedy, 1972).

HERBAGE INTAKE

Sheep in intensive grazing systems do not always achieve their potential DM intake. Hodgson (1982) states that the digestibility and metabolisability of the diet may each vary by a factor of two, whereas the herbage intake of grazing animals may vary by a factor of at least four and restricted nutrient intake is probably the major factor limiting production from grazing animals.

Daily intake is a function of bite size and rate (Hodgson, 1976) and bite size falls with decreasing herbage availability. Hodgson proposed that the relationship between allowance and intake is a function of the rate at which animals graze down to some limiting weight or height of standing crop, below which the prehension of herbage becomes progressively difficult.

In recent studies by Bazely (unpublished), using grass grown in trays, intake was observed over five minute periods. Bite size decreased rapidly and progressively from up to 0.3 g DM/min. down to 0.05 g DM/min. at four minutes. Bite rate also fell from over 60 bites/min. to less than 50. These changes were associated with a decrease in standing crop from 300 g DM/m^2 to 80–120 and a decrease in height from 11.5 to 3–4 cm. The percentage of time spent grazing (as a proportion of total time exposed to trays) decreased from 100 to 55–65 per cent as the sward height approached 4 cm. Figure 3 shows the effect on cumulative intake. It substantiates the conclusion that the limiting height for unrestricted intake is in the range 4–6 cm (Maxwell, 1986).

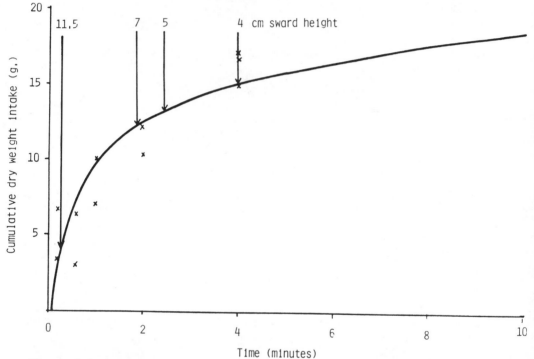

Figure 3. Cumulative intake of grass from a tray. (Bazely, unpublished).

Age and physiological state of the animal also influence the relationship between allowance and intake. The pattern for ewes and lambs is shown in Figure 4 (from Hodgson and Maxwell, 1981). It suggests that ewes will be slightly restricted below a mass of 1800 kg OM/ha (6 cm) and severely restricted below 1200 kg (4 cm). Lambs will become restricted below 1200 kg OM/ha (4 cm).

HERBAGE SELECTION

It is also true, however, that the diet selected by sheep will be better than the value measured for cut samples. Arnold (1960) found that the forage eaten was higher in protein and more digestible than that generally available. Sheep exhibit both selection for species (e.g. white clover) and better areas (site selection) as well as selection within the immediate area (bite selection).

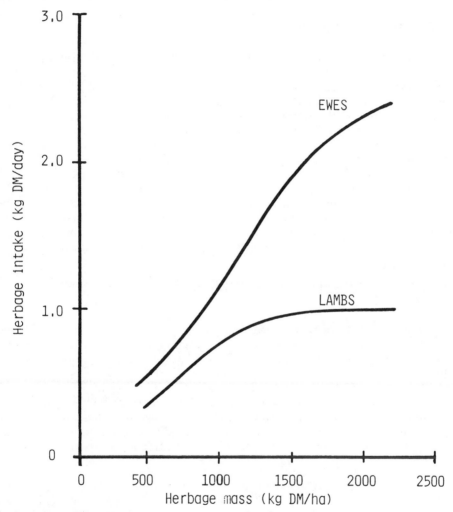

Figure 4. The effect of herbage mass maintained under continuous grazing on the herbage intake of ewes and lambs. After Hodgson and Maxwell, 1981.

In studies at Oxford (Bazely, unpublished) patches (60 × 40 cm) of ryegrass were set up in a regular grid (3 × 3 rows and columns) in a 25 × 25 m paddock. It is apparent from the preliminary results of this work that ewes select better areas and those fertilised with ammonium nitrate or dung/urine. Sward height was also found to be a factor in selection as was sward structure. They showed no selection for patches cut down to pseudostems but they continued to graze preferred patches down below the level of the pseudostems and surrounding areas.

As Hodgson (1982) has pointed out, the opportunity for selection will depend on the intimacy of admixture of plant components, and the ability to select better material will decline as herbage availability is reduced.

THE GROWTH OF LAMBS

Animal performance depends on the supply of energy and protein and its utilisation for maintenance and growth. ARC (1980, 1984) have provided a model for assessment of nutrient requirements based on metabolisable energy (ME), rumen degradable protein (RDP) and undegradable protein (UDP). The limitations of this approach have already been mentioned (Black *et al.*, 1982) but it serves as a basis for prediction which may be further refined.

Given a reasonable estimate of intake, it is possible to predict the growth of lambs from the energy and protein requirements. Given an intake of 1.1 kg DM per day of grass with ME value 11.25 MJ/kg DM (75D) and 180 g CP/kg DM, the predicted growth rate of a 30 kg lamb will be 328 g/day (calculated from ARC, 1980 and 1984). This represents the maximum for lambs of this size and is rarely achieved. A 10 per cent reduction in energy supply (either DM intake or D value) will result in a reduction in growth rate of 59 g/day. Thus the growing lamb will be highly sensitive to both the availability (height) and quality of grass.

EFFECTS OF PARASITISM ON ENERGY AND PROTEIN UTILISATION

Young lambs are highly susceptible to gastro-intestinal parasites. At high stocking rates on contaminated pasture, worm infestation will significantly reduce lamb performance. Continuous larval intakes of 2000–5000 larvae/day produce relatively stable, subclinical conditions. At these levels, Sykes (1983) has shown depressions in intake and reductions in the efficiency of utilisation of ME and protein deposition of up to 50 per cent. There were also effects on calcium absorption and bone growth. Growth rates in excess of 300 g/day have been achieved on clean pasture but these were reduced to 220 g/day or less on dirty pasture (grazed by sheep in the previous year) (Rutter *et al.*, 1976).

MILK PRODUCTION AND EWE BODY CONDITION CHANGES

A more complex model of pregnancy, lactation and body weight change allows prediction of long term changes over the annual cycle of the ewe. The model is based on that of Graham *et al.* (1976) but uses the equations published in ARC (1980, 1984), with additional data from Robinson *et al.* (1980) and Clark (1983). By calculating feed intake, energy requirements and protein requirements in relation to feed supply, it simulates foetal growth, milk production and body weight and composition changes in the ewe. It also predicts when foetal growth or milk production will be reduced due to inadequate energy or protein supply, or insufficient body reserves. Intake of grass, conserved forage and concentrates are predicted on a daily basis, leading into the flow of nutrients shown in Figure 5.

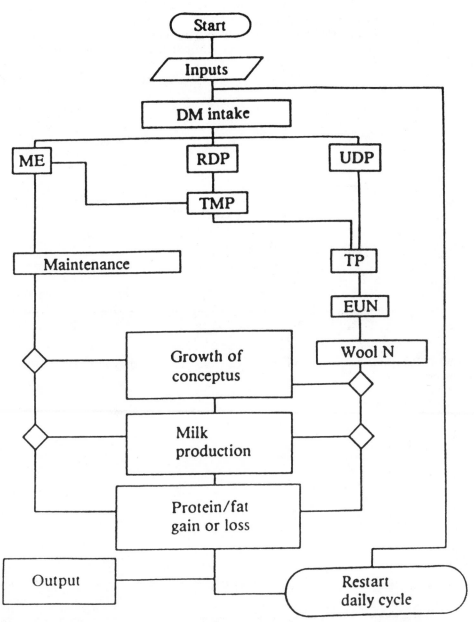

Figure 5. Flow chart of a model of pregnancy, lactation and body composition change in ewes.

The model has been supplemented with a secondary model of lamb growth, again based on ARC (1980). Figure 6 shows the predicted pattern of weight change in a twin-producing ewe from one mating to the next, when summer grazing is unrestricted. The inevitable loss of weight during early lactation (Cowan *et al.*, 1979) is easily retrieved in the summer period, such that body condition is restored well before the start of the next cycle. Milk production (Figure 7) is maximised, with a peak of 3.3 kg/day at 23 days. The growth of the lamb (Figure

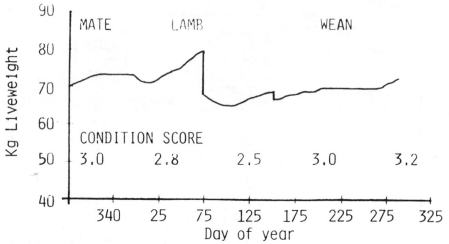

Figure 6. Pattern of live weight and condition score change in the ewe when unrestricted in summer.

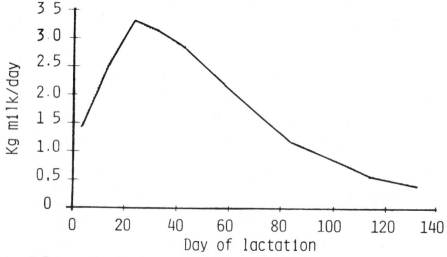

Figure 7. Pattern of milk production by the ewe when unrestricted in summer.

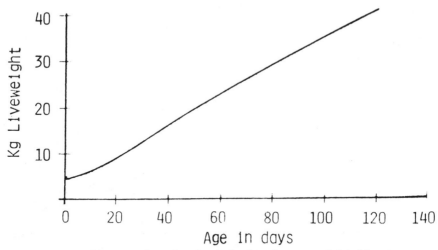

Figure 8. Pattern of live weight gain of twin lambs when unrestricted in summer.

8) is also maximised such that overall growth rate exceeds 300 g/day and the average slaughter age (for twins at 40 kg) is 120 days. Seventy-five per cent of twin lambs will be sold by weaning.

THE EFFECTS OF GRASS SUPPLY AND SUPPLEMENTARY FEEDING ON EWE AND LAMB PERFORMANCE

The use of models to study sheep grazing systems was pioneered by Graham *et al.* (1976) and Edelsten and Newton (1975) and is extensively used in Australia and New Zealand (White, 1985). Newton and Brockington (1976) also describe the use of modelling to provide a logical approach to the study of grazing systems. They described how calculation of herbage availability and intake could be related to maintenance and milk production in the ewe and thence to maintenance and growth of lambs. They used the model to predict the effects of stocking rate and supplementary feeding on lamb growth and liveweight sold, hence predicting the economic consequences of grazing systems. The results were validated against experiments at Hurley.

Similarly, the more recent model of Speedy (1984) may be used to examine the effects of supplementary feeding and grass availability on ewe and lamb performance. Grazing restriction is based on the general model of Hodgson and Maxwell (1981), shown in Figure 4 above. Grass intake is either unrestricted or progressively restricted as herbage mass and sward height are reduced. It is assumed that ewes will be unrestricted at sward heights of 6–8 cm and that slight restriction will occur as sward height declines below 4 cm, declining progressively thereafter.

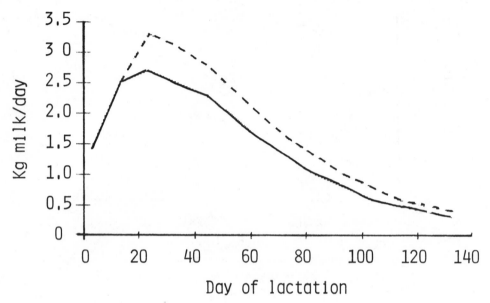

Figure 9. Pattern of milk production by the ewe when supplement is stopped early. (_ _ _ _ unrestricted control; — ewe restricted)

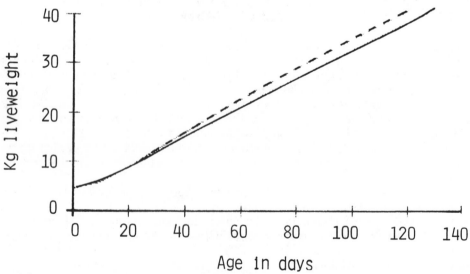

Figure 10. Pattern of live weight gain of twin lambs when supplement is stopped early. (_ _ _ _ unrestricted control; — lamb restricted)

The effects of supplementary feeding in early lactation are shown in Figures 9 and 10. In this case, grazing intake is restricted (0.75) until four weeks after lambing. The unrestricted situation involves feeding 600 g concentrates per day over this period and this has been compared with stopping concentrates two weeks early. The result is a major effect on peak milk production in the ewe, reducing from 3.3 kg/day to 2.7 kg/day. It is assumed that milk production potential is similarly reduced throughout lactation (Graham *et al.*, 1976). There is therefore little effect on the pattern of ewe body weight/condition change. Lamb growth is also only slightly affected because, although milk intake is reduced, the lamb is able to compensate by eating more grass and overall growth rate is only reduced from 303 to 285 g/day. At 120 days, lamb weights are reduced from 41 kg to 38.5 kg. Total milk production was reduced by 16 per cent whereas there was only a 5 per cent reduction in lamb growth.

In the second case, the effects of a moderate degree of grazing restriction throughout the summer grazing period have been examined by applying a factor of 0.75 to grass intake of both ewes and lambs. Supplementary feeding is continued for four weeks so there is no effect on peak production, although some restriction occurs later (Figure 12). Total milk production is reduced by only 5 per cent. However, this results in a major effect on ewe body weight recovery and body condition at weaning. Body condition score is reduced from three to two and ewes fail to restore condition before the next mating (Figure 11). Lamb growth is also affected (Figure 13), being reduced to 227 g/day so that average weight is 33 kg at 120 days (only 17 per cent of lambs will be sold by weaning). It is calculated that this would represent an increase in stocking rate from 14 to 18 ewes with twins per hectare with no increase in grass supply or fertiliser usage.

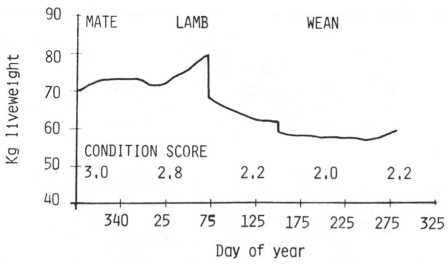

Figure 11. Pattern of live weight and condition score change in the ewe when summer grazing is restricted.

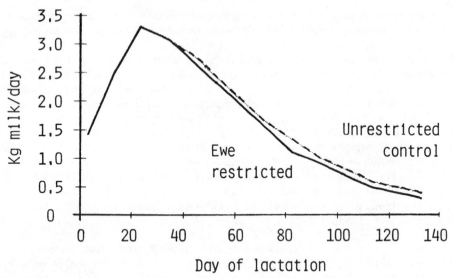

Figure 12. Pattern of milk production by the ewe when summer grazing is restricted.

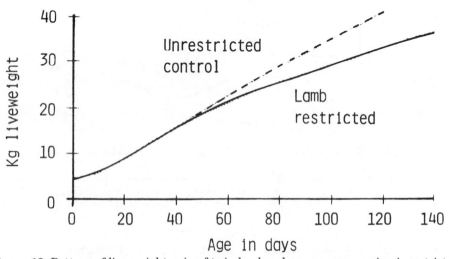

Figure 13. Pattern of live weight gain of twin lambs when summer grazing is restricted.

A more realistic case would be that in which grazing is unrestricted from four weeks after lambing until 10 weeks and then progressively restricted (0.75 reducing to 0.5) thereafter. Figures 14 and 15 illustrate the effects on ewe weight and condition changes and lamb growth. There is again only a small effect on milk production but less opportunity for body weight recovery. Hence ewe body condition is 2.5 at the end of the cycle. Lamb growth is unaffected in the early stages but slows as grass becomes limiting. The result is again a reduction in overall growth (251 g/day to 120 days, 223 g/day to weaning) and the average weight is 34.5 kg at 120 days. This situation is one in which there is a failure to maintain the grass supply through the grazing season.

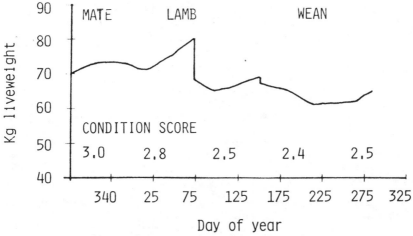

Figure 14. Pattern of live weight and condition weight score change with increasing restriction of grass in mid and late season.

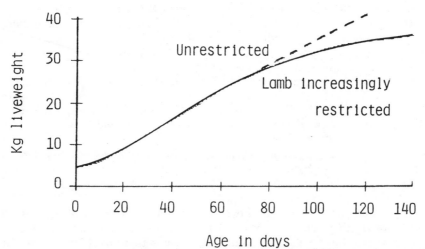

Figure 15. Pattern of live weight gain of twin lambs with increasing grass restriction.

A further run of the model was conducted using the constraint previously described, progressive restriction of grazing, but with ewes weaned one month earlier (Figure 16). In this case, ewe condition is restored to 3.1 by the next mating. The lambs would be moved to aftermaths and should also recover weight gain. These theoretical calculations illustrate the main effects of feed restriction on animal performance in terms of milk production, lamb growth and ewe body weight recovery.

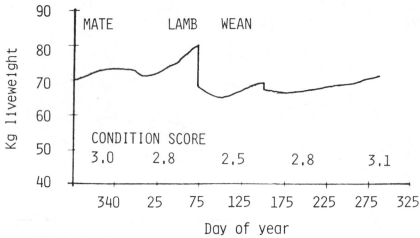

Figure 16. Effect of early weaning or live weight and condition score change of ewe with increasing grass restriction.

METHODS OF AVOIDING GRASS LIMITATIONS

Opportunities exist to change management in order to compensate for grazing limitations. The first decision will be the date of lambing; early lambing increases the need for supplementary feeding but results in earlier sale of lambs, alleviating the effects of late season restriction (Figure 17). Earlier lambing is therefore particularly appropriate in lowland areas subject to summer drought. Once lambing date is decided, seasonal variation in herbage production demands that some flexibility is incorporated into the management system. The timing of cessation of concentrate feeding can be geared to grass availability (sward height) to avoid early restriction. It is suggested that a target height of 4 cm is appropriate (Maxwell, 1986).

Integration of summer grazing with conservation allows flexibility of stocking rate so that sward height may be controlled near to the optimum. In times of shortage, silage areas may be grazed by ewes and lambs whereas, in times of excess, an additional area may be closed for silage.

A further important decision is the date of weaning. In times of shortage, ewes may be weaned early which removes competition between lambs and ewes. In good grass years, later weaning enables the ewes to control the sward for the benefit of the lambs.

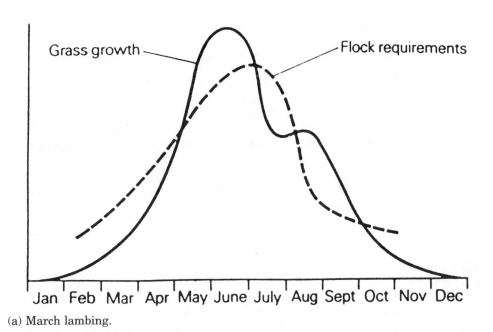

(a) March lambing.

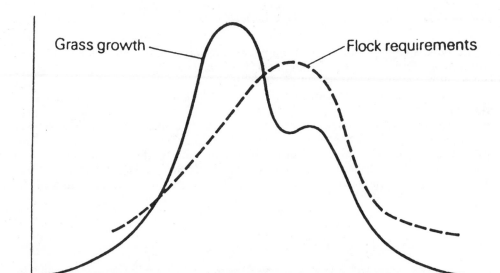

(b) Early lambing.

Figure 17. The pattern of herbage production in relation to total flock requirements (Speedy, 1980).

RESULTS OF EXPERIMENTS

The use of the model to calculate effects of supplementary feeding and grazing restriction further illustrates the value of this technique in studying grazing systems. Experimental results confirm many of the conclusions derived from the model. Clark (1983) showed that major differences in ewe milk production, resulting from different treatments in early lactation, resulted in only small differences in lamb weights at weaning when grass supply was abundant (Table 2). More detailed studies on the effects of supplementation of ewes in relation to herbage supply are in progress (Milne and Mayes, 1986).

Table 2. Milk yield of ewes fed different levels of dietary protein in early lactation and subsequent live weights of lambs (from Clark, 1983)

Treatment	1	2	3	4	SE diff.
Dietary CP g/kg DM	107	134	193	220	
Total milk yield in first					
four weeks (kg)	42.9	49.7	58.6	61.0	5.04
Lamb weights (kg):					
birth	4.5	4.8	5.1	4.9	0.25
four weeks	8.6	9.1	10.4	10.8	0.56
weaning	35.5	34.5	36.3	36.4	1.75

The effects of the timing of management actions on sheep performance was studied over four years in a flock of 180 Greyface ewes by Speedy *et al.* (1984). In three out of four years, grass supply was adequate throughout at a stocking rate of 14 ewes per hectare but in one year (1976) there were important effects of management on ewe body condition changes. In particular, provision of better grazing before mating was important to restore body condition; early flushed ewes averaged 70.8 kg (CS 3.2) compared to 65.0 kg (CS 2.5) for late flushed ewes. This difference continued throughout pregnancy and had an effect on the subsequent birth weight of lambs (4.67 v 4.13 kg twins respectively). This further demonstrates the need to consider the long-term effects of grazing management and the consequences of grass supply for ewe and lamb performance.

FUTURE SYSTEM MODELS

The examples described here show the complexity of the grazing system and the need to study the implications of management decisions on both ewe and lamb performance. Further refinements are needed to improve the model of voluntary feed intake and energy/protein supply (Black *et al.*, 1982), the metabolism of absorbed nutrients (Gill *et al.*, 1985), models of grazing behaviour and selection (Hodgson, 1982; Bazeley, unpublished), and the integrated model of the grazing system (Newton and Brockington, 1976; Graham *et al.*, 1976; Speedy, 1984). The approach serves to integrate the knowledge of fundamental components of the system, demonstrates gaps in existing knowledge and ultimately provides a logical basis for testing and demonstrating the effects of management on the grazing system.

REFERENCES

ARC. (1980) *The Nutrient Requirements of Ruminant Livestock.* Agricultural Research Council. Commonwealth Agricultural Bureaux, Farnham Royal, Slough, UK.

ARC. (1984) *The Nutrients Requirements of Ruminant Livestock. Supplement No. 1.* Agricultural Research Council. Commonwealth Agricultural Bureaux, Farnham Royal, Slough, UK.

ARNOLD, G. W. (1960) The effect of the quantity and quality of pasture available to sheep on their grazing behaviour. *Australian Journal of Agricultural Research,* **11,** 1034–1043.

BARTHRAM, G. T. (1986) Influence of sward height and fertiliser nitrogen use on animal production from mixed grass/clover swards. In: *The Hill Farming Research Organisation, Biennial Report 1984–85.* Edinburgh, UK, pp. 27–28.

BALDWIN, R. L., KOONG, L. J. and ULYATT, M. J. (1977) A dynamic model of ruminant digestion for evaluation of factors affecting nutritive value. *Agricultural Systems,* **2,** 255–288.

BEEVER, D. E., BLACK, J. L. and FAICHNEY, G. J. (1980) Simulation of the effects of rumen function on the flow of nutrients from the stomach of sheep: Part 2 – Assessment of computer predictions. *Agricultural Systems,* **6,** 221–241.

BLACK, J. L., BEEVER, D. E., FAICHNEY, G. J., HOWARTH, B. R. and GRAHAM, N. MCC. (1980) Simulation of the effects of rumen function on the flow of nutrients from the stomach of sheep: Part 1 – Description of a computer program. *Agricultural Systems,* **6,** 195–219.

BLACK, J. L., FAICHNEY, G. J. and SINCLAIR, R. E. (1982) Role of computer simulation in overcoming limitations to animal production from pastures. In: Hacker, J. B. (ed.) *Nutritional Limits to Animal Production from Pastures.* Commonwealth Agricultural Bureaux, Farnham Royal, Slough, UK, pp. 473–493.

CAMMELL, S. B., BEEVER, D. E., LOSADA, H. R., THOMSON, D. J., AUSTIN, A. R., EVANS, R. T., SPOONER, M. C. and TERRY, R. A. (1983) Energy and protein digestion, supply and utilisation on two contrasting forages fed to steers. *Animal Production,* **36,** 501 (Abstr.).

CLARK, C. F. S. (1983) *Ewe nutrition and lamb growth.* PhD thesis, University of Edinburgh.

COWAN, R. T., ROBINSON, J. J. and FRASER, C. (1979) Effect of protein content of the diet on feed intake and milk yield of ewes in early lactation. *Animal Production,* **28,** 453 (Abstr.).

EDELSTEN, P. R. and NEWTON, J. E. (1975) A simulation model of intensive lamb production from grass. *Technical Report No. 17. Grassland Research Institute, Hurley, Maidenhead, UK.*

FERGUSON, J. A. (1974) *Hay quality and the pregnant ewe.* PhD thesis, University of Edinburgh.

GILL, M., THORNLEY, J. H. M., BLACK, J. L., OLDHAM, J. D. and BEEVER, D. E. (1985) Simulation of the metabolism of absorbed energy-yielding nutrients in young sheep. *British Journal of Nutrition,* **52,** 621–649.

GRAHAM, N. MCC., BLACK, J. L. and FAICHNEY, G. J. (1976) Simulation of growth and production in sheep – Model 1: a computer program to estimate energy and nitrogen utilisation, body composition and empty liveweight change, day by day for sheep of any age. *Agricultural Systems,* **1,** 113–138.

HODGSON, J. (1976) The influence of grazing pressure and stocking rate on herbage intake and animal performance. In: Hodgson, J. and Jackson, D. K. (eds.) *Pasture utilisation by the grazing animal. British Grassland Society, Occasional Symposium No. 8*, pp. 93–103.

HODGSON, J. (1982) Influence of sward characteristics on diet selection and herbage intake by the grazing animal. In: Hacker J. B. (ed.) *Nutritional Limits to Animal Production from Pastures*. Commonwealth Agricultural Bureaux, Farnham Royal, Slough, UK, pp. 153–166.

HODGSON, J. and MAXWELL, T. J. (1981) Grazing research and management. In: *The Hill Farming Research Organisation, Biennial Report 1979–81*. Edinburgh, UK, pp. 169–187.

MAXWELL, T. J. (1986) Systems studies in upland sheep production: some implications for management and research. In: *The Hill Farming Research Organisation, Biennial Report 1984–85*. Edinburgh, UK, pp. 155–163.

MILNE, J. A. and MAYES, R. W. (1986) Supplementary feeding and herbage intake. In: *The Hill Farming Research Organisation, Biennial Report 1984–85*. Edinburgh, UK, pp. 115–119.

MORRISON, J., JACKSON, M. V. and SPARROW, P. E. (1980) The response of perennial ryegrass to fertiliser nitrogen in relation to climate and soil. *Technical Report No. 27*. Grassland Research Institute, Hurley, Maidenhead, UK.

NEWTON, J. E. and BROCKINGTON, N. R. (1976) A logical approach to the study of grazing systems. In: Hodgson, J. and Jackson, D. K. (eds) *Pasture utilisation by the grazing animal. British Grassland Society, Occasional Symposium No. 8*, pp. 29–38.

PARSONS, A. J. (1985) New light on the grass sward and the grazing animal. *Span,* **28**(2), 47–49.

ROBINSON, J. J., MCDONALD, I., FRASER, C. and GORDON, J. G. (1980) Studies on reproduction in prolific ewes. 6. The efficiency of energy utilisation for conceptus growth. *Journal of Agricultural Science, Cambridge,* **94**, 331–338.

RUTTER, W., HUNTER, A. G., MATHIESON, A. O., BLACK, W. J. M. and WATT, J. A. A. (1976) Intestinal parasites. In: *Edinburgh School of Agriculture, Annual Report*, pp. 48–49.

SPEEDY, A. W. (1972) *Increasing the frequency of lambing in sheep*. PhD thesis, University of Cambridge.

SPEEDY, A. W. (1980) *Sheep production – science into practice*. London and New York, Longman. 395 pp.

SPEEDY, A. W. (1984) The use of nutrient requirement recommendations to develop a computer model of pregnancy, lactation and body composition changes in the ewe. *Research and Development in Agriculture,* **1**, 95–101.

SPEEDY, A. W., BLACK, W. J. M. and FITZSIMONS, J. (1984) The effects of the timing of management actions on the performance of a grassland based sheep flock. *Journal of Agricultural Science, Cambridge,* **102**, 275–283.

SYKES, A. R. (1983) Effects of parasitism on metabolism in the sheep. In: Haresign, W. (ed.) *Sheep Production*. Butterworths, UK, pp. 317–334.

WHITE, D. H. (1985) Simulation, analysis and management of grazing livestock production in New Zealand. Victoria, Australia. *Dept. of Agriculture and Rural Affairs. Study Tour Report Series, No. 109*, 56 pp.

Silage for Sheep

M. APPLETON
Liscombe Experimental
Husbandry Farm,
Dulverton,
Somerset TA22 9PZ

ABSTRACT

The feeding of silage to sheep has in the past been viewed with considerable suspicion by many farmers. Silage is now becoming more widely used for sheep and from the information available guidelines can be drawn up to make best use of the silage to the benefit of the sheep.

Silage lends itself to most livestock systems because it makes grassland management easier, can be well mechanised and gives a reasonably consistent product year to year. Silage should be well preserved with a good nutritional quality. Supplementary feeding to in-lamb ewes needs to be related to this nutritional quality and to ewe body condition and lamb burden. In theory high quality silage should supply sufficient nutrients without supplementation provided intake is high. More usually supplementation is necessary. Information on protein supplementation has given variable results.

Silage can be fed out-doors but is well suited to housed sheep. Building layout should be related to method of feeding, bearing in mind space requirements, trough space, pen access and the need to keep "dead" space to a minimum.

INTRODUCTION

Feeding silage to sheep is gaining in popularity. Uncertainty and suspicion have given way to confidence based on sound research and development together with increasing practical experience. Guidelines have been formulated which make silage feeding a sound practical system and a viable alternative to hay or root feeding.

In many areas these developments have coincided with the practice of housing ewes and this is where silage feeding fits in most easily. The majority of sheep are still out-wintered and this must not be forgotten.

This paper summarises the information available concerning the most important factors involved in the feeding of silage to sheep, concentrating on the winter feeding of in-lamb ewes. The information is based on a variety of sources: practical sheep farmers, research and development institutions and the advisory services. Some of the main points will be illustrated by reference to work at the Experimental Husbandry Farms, particularly Liscombe EHF where silage has been fed to sheep for the last 25 years.

THE SUITABILITY OF SILAGE

The suitability of silage for sheep depends on a number of factors many of which have a bearing on the overall management of a farm. The relative importance of these factors will vary depending on farm type, climate, elevation, aspect and intensity of farming.

Consistent quality. Within and between year variation in both nutritional and fermentation quality are less with silage than hay.

Weather dependence. Silage can be made under all but the most extreme weather conditions. The use of effective additives together with a good basic ensiling technique can ensure success. Information is available elsewhere on the principles and practice of making quality silage (Liscombe EHF, 1985).

Easier grassland management. A planned approach to silage making is possible as fine weather is not as critical as with hay making. Grassland can be taken out of the grazing cycle for a predicted length of time, from four to six weeks, knowing that it will be available again for grazing at that time. Provided cutting height is not too low then rapid re-growth occurs allowing early re-stocking. Knowing the growth period near optimum responses to fertiliser are possible.

Mechanisation. The complete operation from field to feeding can be fully mechanised if required and, therefore, fits in well with low labour, modern farming operations. The degree to which the procedure is mechanised will depend on individual circumstances particularly the integration with other livestock enterprises and the availability of capital.

SILAGE QUALITY

Nutritional quality and fermentation quality are the keys to success in feeding silage to sheep.

Sheep will reject poorly preserved silage and perform badly unless uneconomic levels of supplementary feeding are provided. Low intakes without supplementation can lead to bodyweight loss, reduced condition, underweight or dead lambs at birth, inadequate milk production for lamb growth and may leave ewes in a condition where they are more susceptible to metabolic and infectious diseases.

Poorly preserved silages can be identified by high pH, above 4.5, and levels of ammonia nitrogen (as a % of total nitrogen) in excess of 10%. Well preserved silage is readily eaten by sheep. Fears of prolapse due to *ad lib* or unrestricted feeding of high quality silage to sheep have largely been unfounded.

High pH, poorly preserved silages or those with high levels of soil contamination can lead to listeriosis. This disease caused by *Listeria monocytogenes* can cause abortion, septicaemia or encephalitis from which there is no cure (Gitter, 1984). The remedy is to ensure silage is well made without soil contamination.

In terms of nutritional quality the targets are 68 D value, 10.8 MJ/kg DM for metabolisable energy and 100 g/kg digestible crude protein. High feed value means less reliance on relatively expensive supplementary feeding.

SILAGE DRY MATTER

Previous recommendations have always emphasised the importance of high dry matter percentage (DM %) for sheep. The results of a series of trials in Europe (Zimmer and Wilkins, 1984) have shown that where effective additives have been used to ensure a good fermentation in unwilted grass then animal performance has been similar to that on wilted silage.

This can be illustrated by reference to experiments at Liscombe EHF which were included in the above paper. Over three years (ADAS, 1981, 1982 and 1983) housed Welsh Halfbred ewes were fed on silages of different DM %.

More wet silage was eaten but dry matter quantities were similar. Ewe weight and condition score changes, twin lamb birth weights and subsequent growth rates were also similar.

Table 1. The effect of silage DM % on the intake and performance of housed ewes (last 8 weeks of pregnancy) 1981–1983

	20% DM	30% DM
Intake (kg/ewe):		
fresh	4.3	3.1
dry matter	0.9	1.0
Ewe weight change (kg)	−1.5	−1.3
Condition score change	−0.4	−0.4
Twin lamb:		
birth weight (kg)	3.8	3.8
lamb growth rate to six weeks (g/day)	260	260

There is some evidence, based mainly on observation in practical situations, that intakes can be much reduced with DM% below 18%. In addition the bedding requirements of housed ewes are markedly increased when wet silage is fed.

At the other end of the scale there can be problems with dry silages and increased aerobic instability. Rapid deterioration with over-heating, moulding and subsequent rejection by the sheep is the usual result.

CHOP LENGTH

Many experiments have demonstrated the benefits of short chop silage for sheep (Deswysen, 1978; Dulphy and Demarquilly, 1973; Apolant and Chestnutt, 1982). The effects have perhaps been most pronounced in comparisons involving big bale silage (Griffiths and Evans, 1983; Morrison et al., 1981). In some of these experiments the effect of chop length was confounded with the quality of the fermentation.

Short chopping is an expensive operation in terms of wear and tear on machinery and fuel use. Slightly longer material may be just as effective if it is well preserved and obtained at lower cost. A recent trial at Liscombe EHF demonstrates this point.

Table 2. The effect of chop length on the intake and performance of ewes (last 8 weeks of pregnancy) 1984

	Chop length	
	25 mm	75 mm
Intake (kg/ewe):		
fresh	4.2	4.1
dry matter	0.80	0.77
Ewe weight change (kg)	−2.6	−1.7
Condition score change	−0.4	−0.3
Twin lamb birth weight (kg)	3.3	3.2
growth rate (g/day)	250	250

Performance was similar on 25 mm and 75 mm silages. This reinforces the suggestion that the quality of the fermentation is the most important factor involved.

SUPPLEMENTARY FEEDING

Care should be taken in the extrapolation of feeding standards based on hay/root feeding into the silage situation. The standards for sheep are still relatively imprecise compared to other species. The volume of data specific to silage for sheep is insufficient to enable precise rationing in all situations.

The starting point in the design of a feeding system must be forage analysis, both chemical and visual. Careful sampling of silage by top to bottom coring prior to laboratory analysis, reinforced by visual examination with a full knowledge of when and how it was made, provides a good base line. Only then can consideration be given to possible methods and materials for supplementation.

Success in rationing can only be judged by the response of the ewes themselves as measured by condition scoring (ADAS., 1984b). This means regular handling to ensure that targets are met. Computer based models for ewe feeding can give general guidance on likely intake and performance but most commercial farms cannot measure intake accurately and the "hands on" approach of condition scoring is still necessary.

The reduced appetite for silage by sheep as lambing approaches is well documented (Forbes *et al.*, 1967; Orr *et al.*, 1983). The replacement rate of silage of high quality is low.

In theory high quality silage alone can supply sufficient nutrients for in-lamb ewes. This has been tried out in practice with mixed results (Stone and Appleton, 1986). It is easier to achieve with housed shorn ewes whose appetite for silage is some 10–15% higher than unshorn ewes (ADAS, 1983).

More usually supplementation is necessary (ADAS, 1983; Apolant and Chestnutt, 1982). The results of experiments on energy and protein supplementation have been expressed in advisory terms in a variety of ways (MLC, 1981; East of Scotland College of Agriculture, 1985; ADAS, 1983).

Energy supplementation is available through a number of materials but barley is the most common. Normally this is fed rolled but recent work (Orskov *et al.*, 1974, Vipond *et al.*, 1985; ADAS, 1980) suggests that whole barley is utilised as well in animal performance terms although some barley passes through the animal undigested.

The theory of protein supplementation suggests that although there is a high level of protein in silage most of this is degraded in the rumen and there will be responses to additions of rumen undegradable protein, particularly those fish-based (East of Scotland College of Agriculture, 1985; School of Agriculture Aberdeen, 1982). Trials elsewhere have not obtained consistent responses to protein in any form (ADAS, 1980; ADAS, 1981; ADAS, 1982; ADAS, 1983).

Table 3 summarises this information.

Table 3.   Supplementing silage

High quality 68 + D	–	Limited energy supplement (no supplement)
Good quality 65–68 D	–	Energy (+ protein)
Medium quality 62–65 D	–	Energy + protein

It is important that at a time when there is a squeeze on margins then all opportunities for economy need consideration such as feeding whole grain and feeding energy alone.

Similarly alternative feeds that may provide more economic supplementation need evaluation.

PATTERNS OF SUPPLEMENTARY FEEDING

Once requirements have been identified then the way in which they are incorporated into a practical feeding system must be considered. For general use and applicability then it must be a simple, easy-to-understand guide. Anything complicated will be of little use in a busy practical situation.

Ewe body condition and lamb burden (detected by scanning) as well as silage quality must be taken into account in deciding on a feeding regime. Table 4 suggests a system for a twin bearing ewe of 55 kg liveweight at six weeks before lambing and in condition score three. For ewes in body condition 2.5 then move down a category of silage quality so that the ewe receives a better quality feed. Similarly for ewes carrying single lambs move up a quality so that supplementary feeding is reduced.

Table 4. Example of a feeding programme

	Silage quality		
	62 D	65 D	68D
Number of weeks feeding pre-lambing	8	6	4
Maximum supplement per ewe per day (kg)	0.7	0.7	0.5
Total requirement (kg)	28	20	10
Type of supplement	Whole barley + protein + mins/vits or Compound	Whole barley + mins/vits	Whole barley + mins/vits

A general purpose mineral/vitamin supplement may be fed with the energy/protein supplement, included in the compound or sprinkled daily on the silage.

It should be remembered that any system should be monitored regularly to assess ewe body condition and adjustments to feeding made to ensure the desired end result is attained.

Level feeding of supplements rather than feeding on an increasing plane is now being advocated (East of Scotland College of Agriculture, 1985).

FEEDING SILAGE

Silage can be fed out-doors but perhaps comes into its own with housed sheep. The change from grazing to housing and silage feeding can be made abruptly providing the ewes have had previous experience of silage and that the silage is of good fermentation. Silage can give rise to foot problems if ewes are not checked pre-housing, footbathed regularly and kept well bedded, particularly when fed on wet silage.

The build up of silage in troughs should be avoided as stale silage can reduce intake. Waste silage should be cleared away regularly. Ewes can be self-fed from clamps or blocks, or various mechanised systems are available (ADAS, 1976; ADAS, 1985).

Building layout should be related to the method of feeding bearing in mind floor space requirements, trough space, pen access and the economic need to keep "dead space" to a minimum.

An example of a sheep shed designed specifically for silage is shown in Figure 1.

Silage may be hand forked from blocks or dispensed from a forage box along the barrier adjacent to the feed passage. Providing silage is available 24 hours a day then the trough allowance means that half the ewes may feed at any one time. Supplements are fed along the barrier and down the walk through feeders to ensure that all ewes can feed at the same time. Other designs can be equally successful (ADAS, 1985).

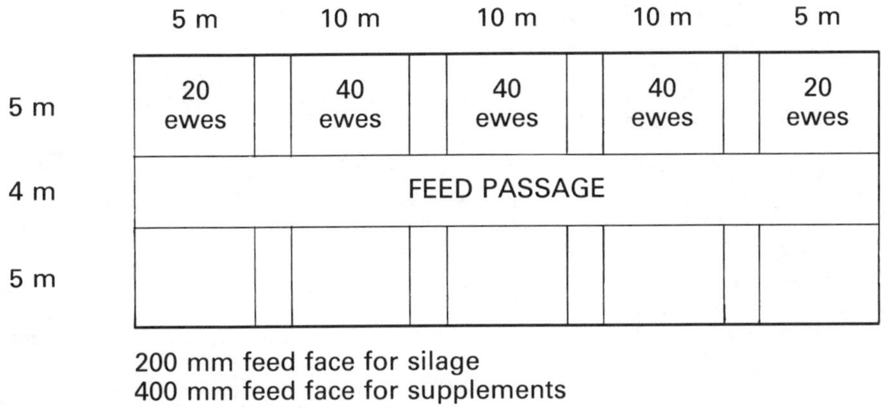

5 m	10 m	10 m	10 m	5 m

5 m	20 ewes	40 ewes	40 ewes	40 ewes	20 ewes

4 m	FEED PASSAGE

5 m					

200 mm feed face for silage
400 mm feed face for supplements

Figure 1. Sheep shed for silage feeding (Welsh Halfbred ewes – 50 kg liveweight)

A change from hay feeding to silage needs to be considered carefully in view of the possible capital spending required for machinery to get into a silage system. Where silage can be introduced for a limited investment then the change may be well justified.

REFERENCES

ADAS. (1980) Agriculture Service. *Research and Development Reports – Sheep.* UK; MAFF.
ADAS. (1981) Agriculture Service. *Research and Development Reports – Sheep.* UK; MAFF.
ADAS. (1982) Agriculture Service. *Research and Development Reports – Sheep.* UK; MAFF.
ADAS. (1983) Agriculture Service. *Research and Development Reports – Sheep.* UK; MAFF.
ADAS. (1984a) Agriculture Service. *Research and Development Reports–Sheep.* UK; MAFF.
ADAS. (1984b) *Condition scoring of ewes.* Advisory Leaflet No. 787. UK; MAFF.
ADAS. (1985) *Silage feeding systems for housed ewes.* South West Region Livestock Technical Note (1985). No. 26. UK; MAFF.
ADAS. (1976) *Mechanised handling and feeding of bunker silage.* Short term leaflet. No. 103. UK; MAFF.
APOLANT, S. M. and CHESTNUTT, D. M. B. (1982) An evaluation of silage for pregnant and lactating ewes. *Annual Report of the Institute of Agricultural Research for Northern Ireland 1981/82;* p. 30–37.
DESWYSEN, A. (1978) The voluntary intake, eating and ruminating behaviour of sheep fed on silage of different chop lengths. *Animal Production,* **26,** 362.
DULPHY, J. P. and DEMARQUILLY, C. (1973) Influence de la machine de récolte et de la finesse de hachage sur la valeur alimentaire des ensilages. *Annales de Zootechnie,* **22,** 199.
EAST OF SCOTLAND COLLEGE OF AGRICULTURE. (1985) *Sheep: Winter Feeding 1985/86.* Edinburgh, UK; EOSCA.
FORBES, J. M., REES, J. K. S., BOAZ, T. G. (1967) Silage as a feed for pregnant ewes. *Animal Production,* **9,** 399–408.
GITTER, M. (1984) Ovine listeriosis in Great Britain. *Proceedings of the Sheep Veterinary Society,* **8,** 28–31.
GRIFFITHS, M. S. and EVANS, C. (1983) Effect of chop length on intake of trough fed silage to in-lamb ewes. *Animal Production,* **36,** 508–509.

LISCOMBE EHF. (1985) *Gass Bulletin No. 2 – Silage.* UK; MAFF.

MLC. (1981) *Feeding the Ewe.* Milton Keynes, UK; MLC.

MORRISON, R. R., HENDERSON, A. R. and HINKS, C. E. (1981) A comparison of big bale and precision-chop silage; silage quality, losses and livestock performance. *Proceedings of the Sixth Silage Conference, Edinburgh,* p. 85–86.

ORR, R. J., NEWTON, J. E., JACKSON, C. A. (1983) The intake and performance of ewes offered concentrates and grass silage in late pregnancy. *Animal Production,* **36,** 21–27.

ORSKOV, E. R., FRASER, C., MCHATTIE, I. (1974) Cereal processing and food utilization by sheep. *Animal Production,* **18,** 85–88.

SCHOOL OF AGRICULTURE ABERDEEN (1982) *1981/82 Annual Report,* p. 46.

STONE, C. and APPLETON, M. (1986) Energy and protein supplementation for shorn, housed pregnant ewes fed silage. *Animal Production,* **42,** 454–455.

VIPOND, J. E., HUNTER, E. A. and KING, M. E. (1985) The utilization of whole and rolled cereals by ewes. *Animal Production,* **40,** 297–301.

ZIMMER, E. and WILKINS, R. J. (1984) *Eurowilt – Efficiency of silage systems: a comparison between unwilted and wilted silages.* Landbauforschung Volkenrode FAL 1984.

Parasite Control in Grazing Systems

M. J. CLARKSON
University of Liverpool,
Department of
Veterinary Clinical
Science, Veterinary
Field Station,
"Leahurst", Chester
High Road, Neston,
South Wirral L64 7TE

ABSTRACT

Although sheep act as host for a wide variety of parasites, the major causes of economic loss are the roundworms, Nematodirus, Ostertagia *and* Trichostrongylus, *the fluke,* Fasciola, *and the sheep tick,* Ixodes.

All these parasites have complex life cycles which are well-known and indicate that a large proportion of the cycle occurs outside the sheep and is thus dependent on temperature and rainfall. Since these meteorological factors also influence grass growth, parasites tend to develop in large numbers on grazing pasture and control schemes must be included in health programmes in order to allow for maximum production. The annual life cycles of these parasites under practical weather conditions in Britain show at what time heavy infections are likely to occur and allow models and forecasts to be made. These forecasts can then be used, together with anthelmintic drugs and grazing management, to maintain growing lambs under conditions of very light parasite challenge and thus increase weight gains and reduce losses.

Health programmes for lowland flocks must include a control scheme for Nematodirus *and* Ostertagia/Trichostrongylus *because these worms occur everywhere.* Fasciola *and* Ixodes *have a more restricted distribution and control schemes leading to eradication are possible.*

INTRODUCTION

Parasites and sheep are inseparable. If we were to examine the faeces of almost any healthy looking sheep, it is highly probable that we would find eggs which, though they look similar, could belong to one or more of a long list of worms, each with exotic sounding names and complicated life cycles. If we were to slaughter a lamb in prime condition and examine each system very carefully, and particularly if we could also look for antibodies to indicate past infection, we would find

57

evidence of small numbers of an even longer list of parasites. This indicates that small numbers of most parasites don't produce disease, that you can't always say which parasites are present by looking for eggs, and, incidentally, stresses the fact that I shall have to be selective in the parasites which I choose to discuss in this paper.

PARASITES OF SHEEP

For convenience, I shall divide parasites into "worms", arthropods and protozoa. Sheep in parts of Britain have representatives of each. "Worms" can further be divided into nematodes (or roundworms), cestodes (or tapeworms) and trematodes (or flukes).

Tapeworms (Cestodes)

I will discuss tapeworms rather rapidly but must point out that this fascinating group have two different stages in their life cycle, each of which lives in a different host species.

Adults. The sheep harbours an adult worm in its intestine, called *Moniezia*, the larval stage of which occurs in a small free living (oribatid) mite, which is found in large numbers on pastures, especially on permanent grazing. This impressive worm, measuring up to 4 metres long, passes white segments in the faeces which are well-known to all sheep-farmers. Despite their size, they rarely cause disease and treatment is seldom warranted. Due to the immense numbers of oribatid mites on the pasture, reinfection occurs immediately after any treatment, but sheep develop a very strong immunity as they get older. The control of *Moniezia* by any method is quite impossible.

Larvae. Sheep also harbour larval tapeworms, all of which occur as the adult stage in the intestine of the dog. These larval stages or cysts are much more dangerous than the adult *Moniezia*, but, again, the dog suffers no noticeable effect from the presence of the adult worms, but passes out large numbers of eggs (in "segments") in their faeces. Sheep become infected by eating the eggs on the pasture and it has been shown in New Zealand that beetles, earthworms and flies can transport these eggs for several kilometres. The cysts develop in different parts of the body and cause diseases like gid, or circling disease (due to *Taenia multiceps*) and hydatid disease in man (due to *Echinococcus*). These parasites, though transmitted by grazing on infected pasture, do not lend themselves easily to control by pasture management but by methods directed against the prevention and treatment of infection by the adult worm in the dog.

Flukes (Trematodes)

Trematodes are far more important than cestodes, and the important worm is *Fasciola hepatica*, the common liver fluke. This bears many resemblances to the tapeworms, especially in that it has a split (or indirect) life cycle in which two hosts are involved. Eggs passed in the sheep faeces develop on the pasture in about a month and the miracidium must infect a special snail, *Lymnea truncatula*, in which a complex cycle of development proceeds, resulting after about two months in the formation of a cercaria, which bursts out of the snail, swims around for an hour or so and then sticks to a piece of grass and secretes a protective layer around itself. Sheep are infected by eating this encysted metacercaria. Since the development of the egg and all the stages in the snail are dependent on a temperature of 10°C or above and a "wet" environment and takes place on the grazing pasture, control of *Fasciola* is very dependent on pasture management. No significant immunity to *Fasciola* develops. Thus *Fasciola* causes acute disease in epidemic years with mortality in all ages of sheep, and chronic disease in ewes resulting in loss of condition and anaemia. Since this occurs at the same time as late pregnancy, it often leads to profound effects on productivity – pregnancy toxaemia, poor colostrum and milk supply and weak lambs. On farms where suitable habitats for snail development occur, it is essential that tight control is exerted. An important feature is that *Fasciola* can infect cattle, goats, rabbits and even man, so "clean grazing" systems don't work in its control.

Roundworms (Nematodes)

Roundworms are found everywhere and it is very difficult to rear lambs free of infection, even in laboratories studying worm infections. It is impossible to maintain sheep worm-free if they graze, and parasite control in grazing animals is essential to the production of prime lamb. This group contains the largest number of different worms, each with almost unpronounceable names and often somewhat different lifecycles. Fortunately, most of them do not cause disease, either because of their method of feeding or because they require special developmental factors such as high temperatures and so are present in only small numbers.

The important roundworms are *Nematodirus*, *Ostertagia* and *Trichostrongylus*, though occasionally, other worms cause severe disease. These worms all have a direct life cycle in that only one host is involved, unlike the tapeworms and the flukes. Most of these worms develop only in sheep (though goats and occasionally, cattle, may harbour them) and this is of key importance in clean grazing systems. In these worms, eggs are passed in the faeces which develop on the pasture to an infective larva which is like a little worm and lives on the pasture or in the soil. In *Ostertagia* and *Trichostrongylus* this development only takes a few weeks, but in *Nematodirus* it takes several months and, quite uniquely in *N. battus*, the infective larva lives inside the egg over the winter and only hatches after a rise in temperature to 10°C, after being exposed to freezing temperatures. This dependence on certain meteorological conditions and the fact that lambs are very much more susceptible than ewes, means that *N. battus* has a single annual cycle, is transmitted from one lamb crop to the next year's lamb crop and suggests that control by grazing management should be successful.

In large numbers all these worms cause rapid loss in condition, profuse scouring and death, but even in small numbers they can have a profound effect upon live weight gain and thus on time to reach slaughter weight. In grazing systems employing high stocking rates and high nitrogen inputs, the limiting factor is often the tightness of roundworm parasite control. Health programmes which we have operated have indicated that this one ingredient may be the most economically significant input and that many excellent farmers are not aware of what is actually a "normal" lamb, with "normal" weight gains, due to the fact that without realising it, they have allowed for the reduction in weight gains or reduced stocking rate or nitrogen application caused by roundworms.

Ticks (Arthropods)

Several arthropods occur in sheep including the cause of the dreaded notifiable sheep scab, *Psoroptes*, but the one which is widespread throughout rough hill grazing areas of Britain, is the (so-called) sheep tick, *Ixodes ricinus*. I say "so-called" because this tick is not at all fussy and can take its meal from many types of warm-blooded animals such as cattle, dogs, man and even grouse. This tick is of great importance in hill areas in that it is active around lambing time and may cause death in young lambs due to the amount of blood which it takes in, though large numbers would be needed to have this effect. However, since it feeds entirely on blood it also takes in certain organisms which are found in the blood and it is the means whereby they are transmitted from one sheep to another.

These tick-transmitted diseases are a cause of great economic loss, particularly in young or susceptible lambs, since acclimatised sheep develop immunity to these agents. Ticks are responsible for tick-borne fever, tick bite pyaemia and louping-ill. *Ixodes* has a three year life cycle and only about one week each year is actually spent on a sheep, the rest being on the pasture – the rough hill grazing. This feature indicates that dipping of sheep with a chemical which kills ticks is, at best, only designed to keep numbers low and that the best method of attack would be to render the grazing unsuitable for the ticks since ticks only occur in certain well-defined areas of the hills. However, this answer is often impossible or too costly and we have to be satisfied with keeping the ticks down to a low number rather than abolishing them altogether. Nevertheless, I know of one hill farm in North Wales where ticks and lamb losses due to tick bite pyaemia were eradicated by ploughing and pasture improvement, though it was, of course, for production reasons that the improvement was carried out.

Coccidia (protozoa)

A brief word about protozoa, the microscopic parasites which are widespread in animals. Coccidiosis is caused by two species of the genus *Eimeria*, though there are several more species which do not cause disease. This parasite has a complex asexual and sexual life cycle in the intestine of lambs which results in the production of millions of resistant microscopic oocysts. These undergo development within a few days on the ground and can then remain infective for many months. The disease is difficult to diagnose but causes profuse scouring in 4–8 week old lambs, usually housed but also in lambs turned out onto the same "convenient" pastures year after year. Heavy infection may occur on these pastures and yearly rotation is advisable.

EPIDEMIOLOGY AND CONTROL

The parasites I wish to consider in detail are the important round worms, *Nematodirus*, *Ostertagia* and *Trichostrongylus* and the liver fluke, *Fasciola hepatica*. We shall need to consider their epidemiology (the factors which give rise to high numbers of parasites) and then control should be logical (though it has to be admitted that it may be economically or technically difficult). The advent of very effective drugs against these parasites and a much more detailed knowledge of their life cycles under practical conditions on farms in Britain, have enabled models to be devised of varying complexity (including computer models) and it is not claiming too much to say that we can now exert a very tight control over these worms.

Nematodirus

I shall take *N. battus* as my example. The fact that only young lambs produce large numbers of eggs which take approximately a year to develop and hatch to the infective stage suggests that a grazing management policy of not grazing ewes and lambs on pastures grazed the previous year by the same group of animals would result in control. This is, in fact, true but anyone who thinks for a moment (or has tried it out in practice) will realise that it is rather impracticable. Accurate records of grazing movements would be needed and the system would break down repeatedly due to availability (or non-availability) of grass in the spring associated with different weather conditions. Nevertheless, if we understand the logic behind it we might be able to find a practical way of achieving our objectives.

Clean grazing systems (see later) with a sheep, cattle and conservation cycle, each of one year, will answer many of these practical problems. However, a sheep/cattle cycle (excluding conservation) has recently been shown by Dr R. Coop at the Moredun Institute to break down for the control of *Nematodirus* due to the ability of *N. battus* to develop in calves as well as sheep, which was thought to be impossible.

The incidence of disease varies from year to year and this always suggests that the weather is important in determining the number of parasites present. Work on modelling of this infection has shown that after an early spring, *Nematodirus* numbers in lambs are low whereas after a late spring, numbers are high and disease is widespread. Models of differing degrees of complexity may be produced but since it is known that the time of hatching of overwintered eggs can be estimated from the measurement of soil temperatures in March to May, a forecast can be made as to the dangerous time of pasture infection. If this is late, when lambs would be eating significant quantities of grass, the MAFF forecast may be used to move ewes and lambs off the pastures which had young lambs on in the previous year for a few weeks, until the larvae have died off.

This may still pose practical problems with rapidly growing grass if the only available method of utilising it is by grazing with susceptible lambs. Under these circumstances, the forecast may be used to institute drug treatment to precede and cover the dangerous period thus preventing the development of large numbers of worms in the lambs, and, incidentally, helping to reduce the number of eggs passed on the pasture, which will improve the situation next year.

61

Ostertagia and *Trichostrongylus*

It should be assumed that these worms are present on all farms, in all sheep. In lowland farms at least, where stocking rates are high, some well-formulated methods of control are essential. Eggs passed by ewes and lambs in spring, develop at different rates because of increasing temperature, so that infective larvae tend to be produced from different batches of eggs at about the same time – usually in July. It is this peak of pasture infection which causes severe parasitism, just at the time that many lambs are being finished for market.

Although many of the infective larvae die off in the autumn, others overwinter on the pasture and perpetuate infection the next year by being eaten by ewes, whose immunity wanes around lambing time, and by young lambs. Thus the cycle is perpetuated. This also explains why the common practice of dosing lambs at 3–4 week intervals in July to September is often unsuccessful since reinfection with large numbers of infective larvae occurs immediately after successful treatment. Complaints that worms have become resistant to drugs is often explained by the fact of immediate reinfection as little clinical improvement occurs.

As in the case of *Nematodirus*, this detailed knowledge of the life cycle of the parasite can be used to model infection and to forecast the time of infection (Thomas and Starr, 1978; Paton and Gettinby, 1983) but, in my view, the pattern is so reproducible and certain from year to year that a forecast will not be of great practical use and a control programme must be used every year to prevent the "July peak" from resulting in severe parasitic disease.

Undoubtedly, the best method of control is by a "clean-grazing" system. The best known method, with years of monitoring and a high degree of success, is that described by workers at the East of Scotland College of Agriculture (Rutter *et al.*, 1984 gives a recent description and appraisal). In this method, a three year rotation of sheep, cattle and hay in which sheep follow cattle and hay follows sheep, prevents sheep from grazing pastures containing infective larvae of sheep worms in the spring. Ewes must be dosed around lambing time to prevent the periparturient rise in egg numbers due to the waning of resistance which would contaminate the new pasture but no dosing of lambs is needed because they are on "clean"-grazing for sheep. There are many practical variations of this basic method (Rutter, 1983). This is an excellent system where there is a combination of sheep, cattle and conservation in balance but many farmers who have sheep as the sole enterprise cannot even consider it. In 1983, I described a system in *The Sheep Farmer* (Clarkson, 1983) for such farms and I quote from it, by permission.

"Unfortunately, many sheep farmers, particularly those who do not also have cattle or do not have much grass for conservation, are unable to benefit from the usual clean grazing systems. In North Wales, for example, where we are developing health programmes for individual flocks with private veterinary surgeons and farmers, the constant cry has been for roundworm control programmes on pastures which have sheep on all the year round.

This led to trials on small pastures which were heavily contaminated with worm larvae to see if worm drenches could be used to produce a clean grazing system on a 'dirty grazing' farm. These small-scale trials, and their application on farms over the last three years, has produced a system which appears to be effective in controlling roundworms and increasing growth rates.

Adult worms produce eggs in the faeces which develop to infective larvae at different rates at different times of the year, depending on temperature. These larvae, if eaten on the grass by a susceptible animal develop in about three weeks to more adult worms.

Adult ewes are very resistant for most of the year, so they can eat a lot of larvae with very few adult worms being produced and therefore very few eggs appear in their faeces – they act rather like vacuum cleaners sweeping up the larvae and not depositing more eggs.

Unfortunately, around lambing time and during early lactation, their immunity becomes reduced and eggs are passed in their faeces, initially from inhibited worms which have stayed coiled up in the wall of their stomach or intestine all winter but now become adult, but also from overwintered larvae which they eat on the grass.

This means that giving a worm drench to ewes at lambing time, so important if the ewes then go onto 'clean grazing', is a waste of money if they go onto dirty grazing. Figure 1 shows the effect of such a dose – the egg count, which gives a rough idea of how many worms are present, falls after the dose but then rises again as the ewes become reinfected. It also shows that the egg count even in untreated ewes falls as the immune response of the ewes become re-established as their milk production falls.

So, to deal with the eggs produced by lactating ewes, which will give rise to large numbers of new infective larvae on the grass in July/August, we shall have to dose more than once, at sufficiently frequent intervals to prevent new infections becoming adult and laying eggs. For practical reasons, we chose two doses after turnout at three weekly intervals and the way these doses reduced egg numbers in the ewes' faeces is shown in Figure 1.

Having dealt with the ewes we need to think of the lambs. They are especially important because they multiply infection much more than the ewes, because they have no immunity. They will eat overwintered larvae on grass soon after

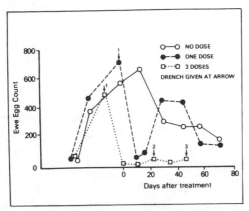

Figure 1. Worm egg counts in faeces of ewes on dirty pasture.

turn out and egg numbers will rise after a few weeks to a very high count, as is seen in Figure 2. In our programme they are dosed with the ewes three to six weeks after turnout and then every three weeks until the majority of overwintered larvae have died off. This varies a little from year to year and from area to area but larvae die fairly rapidly in May, especially if it is dry and most will have died by the end of June.

In our trials we have continued the regular dosing of lambs until the end of June but several of our farmers have stopped dosing a little earlier. The effect of dosing is seen in Figure 2.

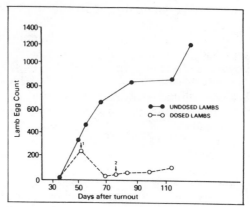

Figure 2. Worm egg counts in faeces of lambs on dirty pasture.

When this system has been incorporated into a health programme for a farm a much higher proportion of prime lambs has been sold for slaughter by September with a resulting increase in profitability, as well as the removal of the problems of store lambs being fattened at the same time as pasture being required for ewes. It also has a cumulative effect as the pastures are much cleaner in the second year as fewer eggs have been passed in the previous year. The system has to be modified to fit into each farm programme, depending on lambing date, stocking rate and availability of pasture."

Under practical farm conditions, this ideal may need to be modified and linked to the turnout of ewes and lambs in batches. Lambs do not eat much grass until they are three to four weeks old so, if they are turned out at a few days old, they do not need to be dosed on the first occasion until they have been on the pasture for six weeks, at the time of the last ewe dose. Some farmers omit the three week dose for ewes due to shepherding and mismothering problems and this will reduce the effectiveness of control slightly.

An even more effective method to administer the worm drug in the early part of the year would be by formulations of continuous or pulse release. Both methods are commercially available for cattle (Paratect, Pfizer; Autoworm, Coopers and

Multidose 130, Syntex) and are being actively pursued by many manufacturers of anthelmintic drugs for sheep. There are greater problems for sheep compared with dairy cattle replacements since both ewes and lambs would have to be dosed and the lambs are so small that technical problems over the size of bolus to be administered will have to be overcome.

Fasciola hepatica

I have already indicated that the life cycle outside the sheep takes three months from egg to metacercaria and needs a suitable snail. It also needs a temperature of 10°C or above, which effectively restricts development in Britain to the May to September period. During this time, the eggs and snails must live in a "wet" environment for a total period of three months, though in the snail, this can be interrupted by spells of dryness.

Empirical work on this basic model by Ollerenshaw and Rowlands (1959) enabled a correlation to be found between rainfall in the May to September period and incidents of acute fascioliasis in the following few months. This was to result in the first forecasting scheme of the MAFF which has been highly successful. More complex and elegant models have been developed (Gettinby and McClean, 1979) but the epidemiological basis of the forecast which is issued annually remains the same. Grazing management may be altered in the light of the forecast which, in effect, gives a few weeks' warning of the peak output of metacercariae from the snails.

The options are to fence off the snail habitats, remove sheep entirely from the pasture if the habitats are extensive, or possibly use molluscicide. Surveys of the farm for habitats must be made and a health programme for the control of fascioliasis produced for each individual farm. The successful operation of such a scheme has been described by Edwards (1968). It is also possible to eradicate snails from farms by drainage and this is the best method when habitats are not extensive. It also improves grass production, of course, and as in the case of ticks, parasite control is an additional benefit.

However, pasture improvement of hill grazing can actually greatly increase the risk of fascioliasis. This is due to the fact that the snail needs alkaline habitats and areas of peat are unsuitable for its development. In areas of hill improvement, the pH has been reduced and extensive snail habitats produced as a result. This necessitates control by anthelmintics, of which we have several highly effective examples, in which the aim is to dose sufficiently frequently to prevent egg production by the flukes so that the snails do not become infected. A successful scheme has been described by Whitelaw and Fawcett (1977).

CONCLUSIONS

I have attempted to show that the interaction between parasites, grazing management and weather conditions is dynamic and that a detailed knowledge of the life cycle in relation to the annual pattern of grass production and utilisation is essential to control. Temperature and rainfall influence parasite development and also influence pasture availability and use. Mathematical models of varying complexity and increasing elegance show that heavy infections of parasites can be forecast. The development of highly effective drugs and different methods of formulation allow a rational combination of strategic dosing and grazing management which can be incorporated into a health programme, designed for individual farms. It is hoped that farmers will demand these services from their veterinary surgeons and that veterinary surgeons will be capable of providing the services.

REFERENCES

CLARKSON, M. J. (1983) Keeping worms under control – dirty grazing. *The Sheep Farmer*, **2**, 25–26.

EDWARDS, C. M. (1968) Liver fluke in sheep: Field trials in Wales on control by planning in advance. *Veterinary Record*, **82**, 718–728.

GETTINBY, G. and MCCLEAN, S. (1979) A matrix formulation of the life cycle of liver fluke. *Proceedings of the Royal Irish Academy*, **79B**, 155–167.

OLLERENSHAW, C. B. and ROWLANDS, W. T. (1959) A method of forecasting the incidence of fascioliasis in Anglesey. *Veterinary Record*, **71**, 591–598.

PATON, G. and GETTINBY, G. (1983) The control of a parasitic nematode population in sheep represented by a discrete time network with stochastic inputs. *Proceedings of the Royal Irish Academy*, **83B**, 267–280.

RUTTER, W. (1983) Keeping worms under control – clean grazing. *The Sheep Farmer*, **2**, 26–29.

RUTTER, W., BLACK, W. J. M., FITZSIMMONS, J. and SWIFT, G. (1984) A clean grazing system for sheep – its development and extension. *Research and Development in Agriculture*, **1**, 41–46.

THOMAS, R. J. and STARR, J. R. (1978) Forecasting the peak of gastro-intestinal nematode infection in lambs. *Veterinary Record*, **103**, 465–468.

WHITELAW, A. and FAWCETT, A. R. (1977) A study of a strategic dosing programme against ovine fascioliasis on a hill farm. *Veterinary Record*, **100**, 443–447.

Decision Rules for Grassland Management

T. J. MAXWELL[1] and
T. T. TREACHER[2]
[1]Hill Farming Research
Organisation,
Bush Estate,
Penicuik, Midlothian
[2]Institute for Grassland
and Animal Production,
Hurley, Maidenhead,
Berkshire

ABSTRACT

At present, sward height offers the best guideline for managing pastures to control both herbage production and animal performance within a system. Sward height affects pasture growth and senescence and hence net production and utilisation per ha. Sward height affects intake of herbage and performance by grazing sheep. Data are presented on the effects of sward height on intake of lactating ewes, on intake of dry ewes in the autumn, and on lamb performance through the season. Swards maintained at different heights alter radically in structure. Reference is made to the effects of height on tiller number and proportion of reproductive tillers.

Sward height profiles through the year are presented for lowland and upland sheep systems together with protocols for management in the critical periods in the season. Reference will be made to systems data indicating that when sward height is used as a management guideline, similar levels of lamb performance can be obtained at a range of stocking rates and nitrogen inputs.

INTRODUCTION

Over the last 2–3 years a considerable concensus of opinion has emerged on the best way to manage pasture in sheep production systems and decision rules have been drawn up. These are based on management objectives which aim to achieve particular sward heights throughout the annual cycle of production. They owe little to conventional grazing and stocking rate experiments and result from work at HFRO and AGRI, which brought together plant physiologists and animal nutritionists to make very detailed measurements of the growth and structure of grazed swards and of the grazing behaviour and intake of herbage by the sheep grazing them. These detailed studies have led to a new understanding of the interrelationships of swards and grazing animals. Subsequently the ideas have been tested in systems in different environments in the UK and appear in general to offer a sound basis for improving grazing management in sheep systems.

SWARD SURFACE HEIGHT

This paper briefly outlines the research that led to the development of decision rules based on the use of sward surface height, outlines appropriate sward height profiles for lowland and upland systems and discusses the problems of controlling sward heights throughout the grazing season.

The complex interactions that occur in grazed swards between photosynthesis, gross tissue production, intake of herbage by grazing animals and death of tissue have been described recently by Parsons (1986), Parsons et al. (1983) and Grant et al. (1983). Figure 1 illustrates the balance of these processes in swards grazed continuously at a range of sward heights. In the tall swards with high leaf area indices (LAI), photosynthesis and gross tissue production are close to maximum but to maintain these high levels, a large proportion of the leaves must remain in the sward to maintain a high level of photosynthesis. Because of the rapid rate of turnover of leaves on perennial ryegrass, which have an average life of only 33 days, a large proportion of the leaf dies and the amount of leaf harvested by the grazing animals is small. In short swards, the LAI is lower and photosynthesis and gross tissue production are reduced. However, the amount of leaf harvested is much greater than in taller swards and less leaf dies.

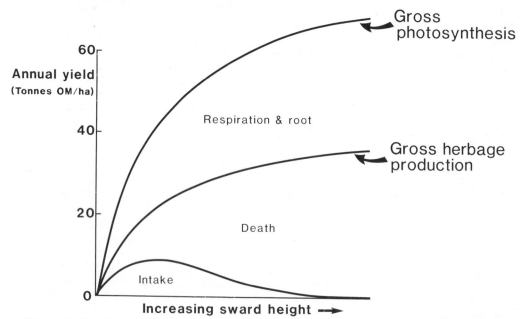

Figure 1. Height, growth and utilisation of a continuously grazed sward. (Parsons et al., 1983).

A number of experiments have indicated that maximal removal of herbage per unit area of land occurs when swards are maintained at sward surface heights of between 4 and 6 cm (Bircham and Hodgson, 1983; Parsons, 1986). Maintaining swards in spring in this height range by continuous grazing leads to major changes in sward structure. Tiller density increases rapidly to 30–40,000/m^2 and stem elongation of reproductive tillers is almost completely eliminated (Figure 2). The development of this structure, which many farmers will consider to be typical of a well-managed sheep sward, has two important consequences. First, the decline in the digestibility of the sward through the season is small and the decline in digestibility of the diet actually selected by the sheep is negligible. For example, in the experiment by Treacher, Orr and Parsons (1986) the organic matter digestibility of the herbage selected from a sward maintained at 5 cm between April and October ranged from 85–75%. Second, the short leafy sward maintains a fairly constant leaf area index throughout the season. This contrasts with the situation in taller swards where the decline in LAI as stem elongation occurs (Grassland Research Institute, 1984) leads to a marked decline in herbage production as the season progresses. In late summer and autumn both short and tall swards will have similar LAI and therefore similar growth rates.

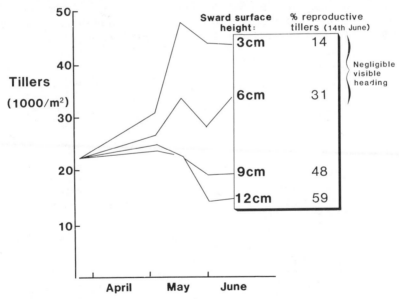

Figure 2. The effect of sward height on sward structure.

The seasonal pattern of herbage production of swards grazed continuously at 4–6 cm is quite different from that of cut swards. Treacher, Orr and Parsons (1986) showed that herbage production of swards maintained by adjusted continuous grazing at 3, 5 and 7 cm throughout the growing season was 15–20% less in May and June than on plots of the same sward cut at four weekly intervals in a standard overlapping sequence (Corrall and Fenlon, 1978). Thereafter production was higher on the grazed swards and the total production over the whole season was very similar on both the grazed and cut areas. Clearly it is wrong to assume the level and pattern of herbage production under cutting represents the potential production of a grazed sward.

Herbage intake and animal performance

Much progress has been made recently in defining the relationships between the structure of the sward and herbage intake by sheep (Hodgson, 1986). Although these relationships are complex and not fully understood, intake of herbage by grazing sheep is correlated with the sward surface height. This single characteristic therefore offers an index of intake and also provides a link with the processes of herbage growth and utilisation.

Figure 3 illustrates the curvilinear relationship between herbage intake in the first 12 weeks of lactation by Scottish Halfbred ewes suckling twins and sward heights maintained at 3, 6, 9 or 12 cm (Penning, 1986). This pattern appears to be typical with steep increases in intake with increases in sward height to 6 cm (Bircham, 1981, cited by Hodgson, 1986) and no increase on swards taller than 6 cm. Performance of the lambs (Figure 4) showed a similar pattern to intake by their mothers with reduced growth on 3 cm swards and no increase in swards above 6 cm. Ewes on the 3 cm sward lost 0.8 of a body condition score whereas the ewes on the taller swards lost 0.2–0.4 of a body condition score.

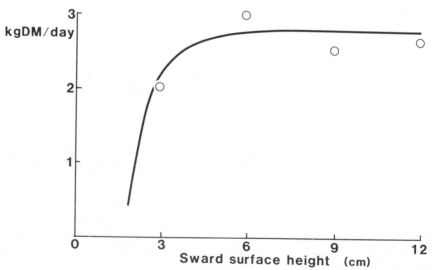

Figure 3. The herbage intake of ewes suckling twins grazed on swards of different heights (Penning, 1986).

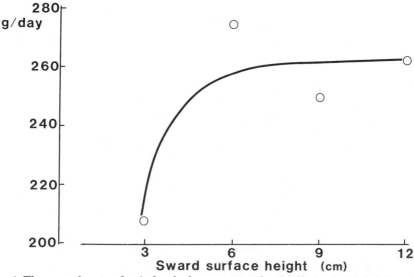

Figure 4. The growth rate of twin lambs kept on swards of differing heights between birth and 12 weeks of age.

Dry ewes, which have a much lower level of voluntary intake than ewes suckling twins, show a pattern of response of intake to sward surface height that is similar to that in suckling ewes (Figure 5). Milne *et al.* (1986) found that daily intake by dry ewes declined from 1.48 kg DM on a 5 cm sward in mid-October to 0.73 kg DM on a 3 cm sward in mid-November. Subsequently work comparing intakes on swards of approximately these heights at the same time found a smaller difference in intake.

OPTIMUM SWARD HEIGHT PATTERN

In spite of the complexity of the interactions between the processes involved in pasture growth and utilisation it is clear that in continuous grazing systems a single criterion, sward height, provides a link between current pasture growth and utilisation per unit area of land, sward structure and hence longer term productivity and intake and performance of the grazing animals. These three factors can be successfully balanced in a grazing system.

In sheep systems during late spring and in summer, pasture utilisation and animal performance can be optimised and a good sward structure maintained if the sward surface height is kept between 4 and 6 cm. The exact application of sward height guidelines will obviously vary with the type of sheep system and pattern of pasture growth. Management guidelines have to be devised to deal with the normal seasonal variation in growth and with short term variations that arise, particularly from temperature in spring and moisture stress in summer.

71

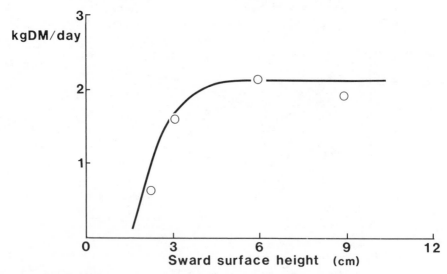

Figure 5. The herbage intake of dry ewes kept on swards of different heights.

Both supplementation and conservation become essential tools for achieving the designated sward heights as far as is possible in the early part of the season. Then in the latter part of the season, when herbage growth rates fall, there is a need to build up some reserve of leafy high quality herbage so that high intakes can be maintained in weaned lambs and in dry ewes before, during and immediately after mating. After the flowering period from mid-June, sward height and herbage mass per unit area of land, can be allowed to increase without causing a major deterioration in sward structure, that is of lasting importance.

The optimum profiles of sward surface height are described for sheep systems in lowland and in upland areas, where the herbage growing season is considerably shorter.

Optimum height profile – lowland systems

The optimum profile of sward surface height for lowland conditions is shown in Figure 6. The management guidelines relating to the five main periods of the grazing year and sheep production cycle are:

1. *Winter grazing (late pregnancy).* Grazing of the main spring and summer area at this time will depress spring growth so, if possible, the flock should be housed or grazed on a separate sacrifice area.

2. *Early spring (post-lambing).* There are obviously large variations in the time when growth starts in the spring. Work at HFRO (Milne *et al.*, 1981) suggests that no lasting response of animal performance to supplementation occurs once the growth of the sward is sufficient to maintain a minimum height of 4 cm, so supplementation should be phased out once this height can be maintained.

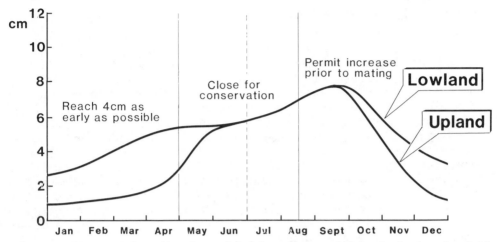

Figure 6. The annual profile of sward height recommended for lowland and upland systems.

3. *Mid-lactation.* Management in this period is critical if the level of utilisation is to be high and flowering and a subsequent decline in tiller numbers and structure prevented. High utilisation and good sward structure are both achieved by keeping swards below 6 cm and nearer to 4 cm rather than above 6 cm, when the risk of a decline in structure is great, especially on mixed grass/clover swards. Height can be controlled by increasing stock numbers, but this is unlikely to be feasible on most farms. So areas must be taken out of grazing and closed for conservation, preferably as silage, as the aftermath will be available for grazing earlier. The problem of decision rules relating to the proportion of the grazing area to close for conservation is discussed below but limited experience suggests that this problem is less important in lowland conditions than in uplands ones, where the peak of growth is delayed.

4. *Weaning and ewe recovery phase.* In this period the performance of lambs still suckling their mothers is unlikely to be reduced until heights fall below 4 cm. This height can generally be achieved by extending grazing to include regrowths after conservation. There is little information on the response of weaned lambs to sward height, particularly of regrowths, but their performance is likely to be reduced if sward height falls rapidly, as little highly digestible leaf will remain and they are forced to consume stem. Dry ewes will maintain high intakes on swards above 4 cm. Later in the period, however, it is desirable that sward height is increased to about 8 cm to build up a reserve of good quality herbage to maintain intake in the period around mating.

5. *Pre- and post-mating phase.* Rapid declines in sward height should be avoided during mating and immediately afterwards, as intake by the ewes may fall below a maintenance level. Then, in the approach to winter, all swards should be grazed down so that they are at about 3 cm at the end of the year. Thus all the herbage that is left in late winter is utilised and the sward is in the best condition to survive the winter and make good growth in the spring.

Optimum height profile – upland systems

These are broadly similar in principle to the guidelines recommended for lowland systems but differ in relation to the shorter period of annual herbage growth.

Thus in late winter it is important that the main spring and summer grazing areas are rested if at all possible from late February until lambing. After lambing, though this may be later than in the lowlands, a longer period of supplementation can be expected to be necessary until sward height reaches 4 cm. To shorten the period of supplementation and improve grass growth nitrogen fertiliser should be applied up to 80 kg/ha in the spring probably in two applications the first being made when 10 cm soil temperature reaches 5.5°C.

Though the peak of growth in the uplands is later than in the lowlands it is often dramatic and prompt action is required in adjusting stock numbers and closing areas for conservation to maintain sward heights within the 4–6 cm limit. Adjustment of stock numbers and closure of surplus grazing areas may have to extend to a second cut of silage or hay to maintain swards until weaning in a leafy state and within the 4–6 cm limit.

During the recovery phase and the period leading up to mating an accumulation of grass is necessary to provide sufficient grass during the pre- and post-mating periods to improve and maintain ewe body weight and condition. Experience suggests that for the uplands an 8 cm sward needs to be achieved by mid-September to avoid sward height being reduced to below 3 cm prior to mating being completed. Stocking rates should be adjusted to avoid this occurring but if this is not possible, supplementation at a rate of not less than 300 g/head may be introduced to avoid a reduction in potential reproductive performance.

THE RESULTS IN PRACTICE

An experiment at the Bronydd Mawr Research Centre in South Wales (Maxwell *et al.*, 1985) investigated the effects of using two annual levels of nitrogen, 100 kg N compared to 200 kg N/ha, at either a stocking rate of 12 or 20 Brecon Cheviot ewes/ha. During lactation sward height was maintained within the same range for all treatments by closing surplus areas for conservation. During the autumn ewe live weight was maintained by offering a cereal/protein supplement when sward height declined below 3.5 cm.

Despite large variations in overall summer stocking rate and annual nitrogen application, lamb growth rates and weaning weights were maintained at similar levels when the grazed sward during lactation was held within the same specified limits (Table 1). Output per unit area was affected by overall stocking rate and the proportions of the areas closed to control sward height were affected by both stocking rate and nitrogen level. Subsequent performance was not significantly affected by stocking rate but there is a suggestion that nitrogen level may have increased reproductive performance.

Results with larger ewes at Hartwood in Central Scotland e.g. the Border Leicester × Scottish Blackface (Greyface) ewe, confirm that animal performance, particularly lamb growth and output of lamb per hectare, can be predictably assured if grass is managed according to the sward height profile given in Figure 6.

Table 1. Ewe and lamb production (1984) Bronydd Mawr

	20		12	
Stocking rate (ewes/ha)				
Nitrogen level (kg N/ha)	200	100	200	100
Lamb : ewe ratio	1.20	1.20	1.20	1.20
Lamb live weight (kg)	29.3	28.8	29.6	29.5
Weaning weight lamb per hectare (kg)	705	688	420	429
Pre-mating ewe live weight (kg)	46.8	44.9	49.2	49.2
Condition score	2.8	2.7	3.1	3.0
Potential lambing percentage (1985)	137	114	125	120
Proportion area conserved	0.19	Nil	0.50	0.40

In general these systems have produced predominantly forward-store lambs. This is in part due to the experiments being conducted in the uplands where spring growth of grass is late and where there is a heavy reliance on supplementary feed for the first 3/4 weeks of lactation. Supplements are no substitute for adequate amounts of grass. Secondly, swards have been managed at the lower end of the 3–6 cm range recommended. This is ideal for the production of a high proportion of store lambs which grow well after weaning and reach appropriate market weights at the time of higher lamb prices. To catch the early high lamb prices of the late spring and summer it is probable that sward heights of around 5 cm will have to be maintained.

The results of using the sward height profiles recommended show that sward surface height can be used to more objectively manage grass for sheep and provides a practical basis for controlling animal performance and improving the efficiency of grass utilisation irrespective of stocking rate and level of nitrogen used.

CONTROLLING SWARD HEIGHT

The main way of controlling sward height is through the adjustment of ewe numbers per grazed unit area throughout the grazing season in relation to grass growth. Reference has already been made to the use of conservation and the closing of surplus grazing areas to achieve this. However, the rate of adjustment in stock numbers (and in the spring size of area closed for conservation) in response to an increase or decrease in sward height, is dependent upon temperature, soil moisture and the amount of nitrogen applied and the consequent effect on grass growth. Since farmers cannot measure grass growth directly or predict with confidence its rate of change throughout the grazing season a simple approach to the problem has been suggested by Hodgson *et al.* (1986).

Table 2 indicates the changes in stocking rate (expressed as a percentage of current stocking rate) needed to respond to change in sward height between successive measurements, taking into account any difference between current sward height and target height. The adjustments should help to keep sward heights close to target over a sequence of successive weekly measurements.

Table 2. Stocking rate adjustments to compensate for sward height changes under continuous stocking management

| | | % Changes in height over previous week | | |
		Decrease	No change	Increase
Current height	High	0	+10	+20
	On target	−10	0	+20
	Low	−20	−10	0

Further work is necessary to improve the precision of these adjustment decisions with the possible use of weather forecasting techniques in relation to soil moisture changes, and incoming radiation. Simple ways of predicting responses to nitrogen application and the nitrogen status of plants and soils are also needed.

An alternative to the use of conservation as a means of controlling sward height which is often used on upland farms is the use of cattle. So often, however, they are used at the point when sheep grazing management is out of control and where seed heads are already in evidence. This is too late. Used earlier, cattle can control swards for sheep within the 4–6 cm limit: there is however, a penalty to be sustained in beef cattle performance (Wright *et al.*, 1986; Wright and Russel, 1986) (Figure 7). This may or may not be acceptable depending on the calf growth rates in the late part of the season when sward heights are increased and the extent to which reduced levels of performance are economically acceptable.

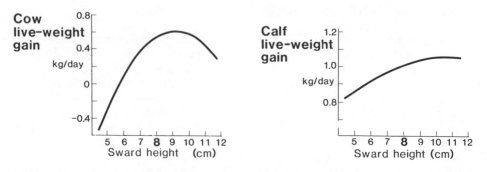

Figure 7. The effect of sward height on cow and calf performance.

CONCLUSIONS

The sward height profiles recommended for both lowland and upland sheep production systems are based on sound biological principles and have been shown to work in different environments, with different breeds of sheep and with varying levels of fertiliser inputs. There is a need, however, to obtain more information with respect to the effect of rate of herbage growth on intake particularly at low sward heights. The influence of sward height on the intake and growth of the weaned lamb has only just begun to be investigated in detail and more will need to be done. There is also a need to investigate the intake of ewes and lambs grazing silage and hay aftermaths.

The ability to manipulate the seasonal distribution of grass in a predictable way requires more specific information on the relationships between plant and soil nitrogen and herbage growth. The quantities of inorganic nitrogen that need to be applied to obtain the required responses in herbage growth to more closely match grass demand and supply grass throughout the season could then be more predictably determined.

Nevertheless, despite these deficiencies, greater objectivity in management can be achieved using the knowledge we already have. Systems can be designed to produce consistent and predictable levels of animal performance, output per unit area and winter forage over a range of inputs but the efficiency with which grass is used can be maintained at a very high level irrespective of the levels of inputs used.

REFERENCES

BIRCHAM, J. S. and HODGSON, J. (1983) The influence of sward conditions on rates of herbage growth and senescence in mixed swards under continuous stocking management. *Grass and Forage Science*, **38**, 323–331.

CORRALL, A. J. and FENLON, J. S. (1978) A comparative method for describing the seasonal distribution of production from grasses. *Journal of Agricultural Science, Cambridge*, **91**, 61–67.

GRANT, S. A., BARTHRAM, G. T., TORVELL, L., KING, J. and SMITH, H. K. (1983) Sward management, lamina turnover and tiller population density in continuously stocked *Lolium perenne* dominated swards. *Grass and Forage Science*, **38**, 333–344.

GRASSLAND RESEARCH INSTITUTE. (1984) *Annual Report 1983/84*, pp. 43–45.

HODGSON, J. (1986) Grazing behaviour and herbage intake. In: Frame, J. (ed.) *Grazing, Occasional Symposium No. 19, British Grassland Society*, pp. 129–137.

HODGSON, J., MACKIE, C. K. and PARKER, J. W. G. (1986) Sward surface heights for efficient grazing. *Grass Farmer* (BGS Publication No. 24) 5–10.

MAXWELL, T. J., SIBBALD, A. R., MORGAN, E., JONES, J. R. and JAMES, E. (1985) The effects of stocking rate and level of nitrogen use on the output per ewe and per unit area. In: *Efficiency in Grassland Production and Utilisation: 2nd Agricultural R & D Conference, Bangor, April 1985*, pp. 22–23. Abstract.

MILNE, J. A., MAXWELL, T. J. and SOUTER, W. (1981) Effect of supplementary feeding and herbage mass on the intake and performance of grazing ewes in early lactation. *Animal Production*, **32**, 185–195.

MILNE, J. A., SIBBALD, A. M., LAMB, C. S., MCCORMACK, H. A., MAYES, R. W. and LEES, J. A. (1986) The herbage intake of ewes grazing perennial ryegrass swards and when given supplements during lactation and in the autumn. In: J. Frame (ed.) *Grazing, Occasional Symposium No. 19, British Grassland Society*, pp. 124–128.

PARSONS, A. J. (1986) The physiology of grass growth under grazing. In: Frame, J. (ed.) *Grazing, Occasional Symposium No. 19, British Grassland Society*, pp. 3–13.

PARSONS, A. J., LEAFE, E. L., COLLETT, B. and LEWIS, J. (1983) The physiology of grass growth under grazing. 2. Photosynthesis, crop growth and animal intake of continuously grazed swards. *Journal of Applied Ecology*, **20**, 127–139.

PENNING, P. D. (1986) Some effects of sward conditions on grazing behaviour and intake by sheep. In: Olafur Gudmundsson (ed.) *Grazing Research at Northern Latitudes*, pp. 219–226, Plenum Publishing Corporation.

TREACHER, T. T., ORR, R. J. and PARSONS, A. J. (1986) Direct measurement of the seasonal pattern of production on continuously-stocked swards. In: J. Frame (ed.) *Grazing, Occasional Symposium No. 19, British Grassland Society*, pp. 204–205.

WRIGHT, I. A. and RUSSEL, A. J. F. (1986) Response of spring calving cows and their calves to sward height. *Animal Production*, **42**, 464. Abstract.

WRIGHT, I. A., RUSSEL, A. J. F. and HUNTER, E. A. (1986) The effect of winter feed level on weaned suckled calves grazed at two sward heights. *Animal Production*, **43**, 211–224.

White Clover and Sheep Production

J. E. NEWTON[1] and
D. A. DAVIES[2]
[1]Animal and Grassland
Research Institute,
Permanent Grassland
Department, North
Wyke, Okehampton,
Devon EX20 2SB
[2]Welsh Plant Breeding
Station, Plas Gogerddan,
Aberystwyth,
Dyfed SY23 3EB

ABSTRACT

Reasons for using white clover in grassland for sheep are well documented. Herbage production on grass-clover swards without fertiliser-N is similar to pure grass receiving about 200 kgN/ha. Better individual lamb live weight gain on swards containing clover of around 25% is due to higher intake and protein levels. Clover based systems have resulted in a greater proportion of finished lambs from grazing and with a higher killing-out percentage. However, to achieve these benefits, it is important to establish and maintain swards with a good clover content.

Establishment, the effects of variety, grazing management and companion grass type on clover persistence and productivity are discussed. Although rotational grazing seems to be advantageous there are examples of good clover contribution under continuous stocking. Differences between clover varieties, depending on leaf size, are considerable with the small leaved types more suitable for continuous stocking, especially in the uplands. From work at WPBS and AGRI it is suggested that target lamb carcass outputs of 350 kg/ha in the uplands and 500 kg/ha in the lowlands are possible from grass–clover swards under low N inputs. These are considerably higher than those currently achieved by most producers. The challenge now is to improve the reliability of white clover and to develop systems of utilisation so as to achieve these outputs consistently in practice.

THE CASE FOR USING WHITE CLOVER IN GRASSLAND

The use of white clover to increase herbage production in systems where little nitrogen fertiliser is used has long been practised; typical yield levels are given in

Table 1. Nitrogen fixation by rhizobial bacteria allows the mixed sward without fertiliser N to give yields similar to those of pure grass swards receiving about 200 kg N/ha per year (Hoglund *et al.*, 1979, Morrison *et al.*, 1985). There is, however, a wide range depending on soil, climate and amount of white clover present (Cowling, 1982). The use of white clover instead of fertiliser-N has also been shown to improve the nitrogen economy of the system, with less nitrogen being lost to the atmosphere or by leaching (Ryden, 1983).

Table 1. A comparison of herbage yields

	t DM/ha	N equivalent
Grass + "0" N	1.8	
Grass + 200 kg N	7.2	
Grass + white clover (uplands)	5.0	180
Grass + white clover (lowlands)	7.0	180

Growing realisation of the increased feeding value of legumes compared with grass is a further important aspect of the case for using white clover. Its inclusion in swards grazed by weaned lambs and ewes and lambs has consistently improved live weight performance of animals (Table 2 and Newton *et al.*, 1985). The reasons for this better performance, based on higher intake and higher protein levels in the clover, have been reviewed recently by Thomson (1984). The largest difference in intake between white clover and perennial ryegrass is likely to come in the second half of the year and in situations where the grass has been allowed to become mature. The gut-fill of lambs fed on white clover has been shown to be much less than that with perennial ryegrass (Gibb and Treacher, 1984), and to result in a higher killing-out percentage.

Table 2. A comparison of lamb live weight gain on grass and grass–clover (g/hd/day)

	Grass	Grass/clover	% Increase	Time
Uplands	70	107	53	August–November
Lowlands	53	109	106	August–November
Lowlands	163	241	48	June–September

(From Davies et al., 1986; Davies and Evans, 1986; and Betts et al., 1983)

In order to achieve these benefits, there is an obvious need for swards to contain substantial proportions of white clover. Carcass gain by lambs has been shown to be directly related to the proportion of white clover in the diet (Gibb and Treacher, 1984) and N-fixation is often directly related to the quantity of white clover grown (Cowling, 1982). Although Curll *et al.* (1985b) found that total herbage yield increased from 6 t DM/ha with 10% clover to 11 t with 45% clover, the exact relationship between clover proportion and herbage yield is likely to vary with the supply of N to the sward from soil organic matter, returned excreta and fertiliser.

Subsequent paragraphs discuss clover establishment, the effects of variety and management on clover persistence and sward productivity; finally, consideration is given to herbage intake and production from clover-based swards.

CLOVER ESTABLISHMENT

The establishment and early management of white clover has been well-documented (Scottish Agricultural Colleges, 1983), but there is a compromise situation between earliness of sowing, which leads to better establishment, and minimising loss of production during the year of sowing. Sowing after first-cut silage will give a better chance of good establishment than after second-cut silage, but the silage yield will be reduced. Use of the Hunter drill to slot-seed white clover into permanent grassland has given impressive results. Sheldrick *et al.* (1987) have obtained swards with over 40% white clover one year after seeding, but there are large effects of management on the rate of development of the clover.

THE EFFECT OF MANAGEMENT AND CLOVER VARIETY

Trials using cutting, rotational- and continuous-grazing by sheep (Evans and Williams, 1984) have shown that large-leaved clovers (Olwen) and medium-leaved (Menna and S 100) have ranked higher than small-leaved clover (S 184) under cutting and rotational grazing, but that the ranking order has been reversed under continuous grazing, with Olwen doing particularly badly (Table 3). Dry matter yield of clover was reduced from 4.7 t DM/ha with cutting to

Table 3. The interaction between clover leaf size and management

	Olwen (L)	Menna (M)	S100 (M)	S184 (S)
	Yield (t DM/ha)			
Cutting only	5.5	4.4	4.7	3.8
Continuous grazing by sheep	0.8	2.4	2.3	2.4
	Stolon length (m/m^2)			
Cutting only	69	128	170	212
Continuous grazing by sheep	7	20	18	42

L = Large-leaved   M = Medium   S = Small
(From Evans and Williams, 1984)

2.3 t under continuous grazing. The use of continuous grazing with sheep reduced stolon length by 90% for Olwen, and even with S 184 the reduction was 80%. More stolon was present under both managements with the smaller-leaved clovers.

Advantages for the use of rotational grazing rather than set-stocking were also found by Newton *et al.* (1985) using Blanca white clover, and in recent experiments at North Wyke with Huia white clover. The tendency for clover to be favoured with rotational grazing probably arises through this management ensuring a longer period of rest from defoliation. Moustapha *et al.* (1969) and, more recently, Ryle *et al.* (1985) have shown that after clover has been defoliated it takes at least six days before the original level of N-fixation is re-attained, and that the rate of photosynthesis is similarly reduced by approximately 90% after defoliation. If, as has been shown by Curll and Wilkins (1982), the clover plant is defoliated every 4–5 days when continuously grazed at a high stocking rate and every 7–8 days at a lower stocking rate, then one would expect that N-fixation and sward productivity would be considerably reduced, unless a rest period is introduced.

Effects of clover morphology on response to grazing have already been noted, and although clover is often favoured by rotational grazing, the use of such a management practice does not appear to be essential. Thus Curll *et al.* (1985a and b) and Curll and Wilkins (1985) using well-established grass–clover swards found that with a stocking weight of c 1.5 t LW/ha clover stolon density was maintained over four years of experiments (although reductions occurred at higher stocking weights), and Parsons (personal communication) has found satisfactory clover persistence over two years in swards continuously stocked to maintain sward surface heights of 3, 6 or 9 cm. Even with basically continuous grazing systems, periods of rest can be achieved through integration of grazing with conservation. Curll and Wilkins (1985) found that the inclusion of a rest period of eight weeks increased clover content by 30%, compared with continuous grazing at a high stocking rate.

It is now clear that autumn and winter management is important for clover persistence. Grass continues to grow later into the year than clover, and unless the sward is grazed down, clover stolon length will be reduced during the winter, giving a weakened presence in spring.

COMPANION GRASS

Work at Aberystwyth is showing that tetraploid and early-flowering diploid varieties of perennial ryegrass are more compatible with white clover than later diploids (Davies and Evans, 1986), possibly because they tiller less, and the small leaved white clover Kent makes a larger contribution than Huia or Menna (medium-leaved) when continuously-grazed by sheep (Table 4). Effects of different companion grasses were also discussed by Frame and Newbould (1985) and Collins (1985). In general, clover contents are higher with tetraploid than with diploid ryegrass.

Table 4. The effect of grass and white clover variety on clover % under continuous grazing by sheep.

Grass	Clover % in the dry matter		
	Huia (M)	Menna (M)	Kent (S)
Aurora (v. early)	14	13	20
Frances (early)	11	6	19
Talbot (medium)	6	6	22
Melle (late)	7	5	18

M = Medium leaf   S = Small
(Davies and Evans, 1986)

CLOVER IN THE DIET

Sheep have been shown to increase the proportion of clover in their diet compared with that in the herbage available (Milne *et al.*, 1982; Curll *et al.*, 1985a). This occurs more at low than at high levels of clover in the sward, such that with 10% of clover in the sward intake of clover is predicted to be 25%, and at 40% of clover in the sward to be about 45% depending on the way in which the clover is presented.

Three factors appear to contribute to this pattern. Firstly, the content of clover is often higher in the upper rather than the lower sward horizons, with the upper horizons likely to be more severely grazed. Secondly, Milne *et al.* (1982) found that even within a particular sward horizon, the clover contained in the diet was higher than that in the herbage available, indicating positive selection for clover. A third possibility is the concentration of grazing on clover-rich areas of the sward, as indicated by Clark and Harris (1985).

The proportion of clover in the diet can be increased through offering sheep a sward with high herbage mass. When a grazed sward is rested during a period of active growth, as in a rotational system, the proportion of clover increases in the top half of the sward (in which grazing is mainly concentrated) (Milne *et al.*, 1982). Likewise Curll *et al.* (1985a) with continuous grazing found that clover in the diet increased with increase in herbage mass. However, care must be taken to ensure that systems involving high levels of herbage mass do not involve excessive herbage loss through increased senescence. In this context, rotational systems involving forward creep grazing by lambs are attractive, as this grazing method should facilitate a high content of clover in the diet of the lambs whilst letting the ewes graze the swards severely and thus avoid high losses through senescence.

FIELD TRIALS WITH DIFFERENT MANAGEMENT SYSTEMS

An experiment comparing rotational grazing, with forward creep for the lambs, with set-stocking at 16 ewes and 32 lambs per ha on a grass–white clover sward,

Table 5. The effect of grazing system on lamb growth rate from grass–white clover

	Lamb growth (g/hd/day)		Carcass output (kg/ha)
	0–8 weeks	0–sale	
Set-stocking	330	200	416
Rotational grazing	332	309	553

Ewes at 16 per ha with twins

showed a marked advantage in favour of the lambs being rotationally-grazed from birth to sale, with the advantage coming from June onwards (Table 5). The proportion of clover in the next paddock to be grazed in the rotational system was 46% in June and 55% in October, compared with 7% over the whole area in June and 5% in October on the set-stocked area (Newton *et al.* 1985). In a similar experiment in Devon, lamb growth rate from birth to sale was superior on a sward that was rotationally-grazed compared with one that was set-stocked at 14 ewes per ha over three years with 47, 75 and 85% of lambs reaching a target weight of 38 kg on the rotational system and 32, 24 and 21% on the set-stocked. There was also more clover and stolon on the rotational system (Table 6). As noted earlier, however, advantages of this magnitude from rotational grazing are unlikely to occur in all circumstances.

Table 6. The effect of grazing system on stolon length (m/m^2) from a grass–white clover sward

	Set stocked	Rotationally grazed
1983 (initial value)	5.6	2.5
1984	1.8	11.0
1985	6.6	42.6

Stocking rate 14 ewes + 26 lambs per ha

TARGET OUTPUTS WITH GRASS–CLOVER SWARDS

Work at WPBS and AGRI suggests target lamb carcass outputs from grass–clover swards with less than 50 kg N/ha of 350 kg/ha for the uplands and 500 kg/ha for the lowlands. This target is being achieved in the uplands from 40 kg LW ewes stocked at 18/ha having a lambing percentage of 150 and lamb carcase weight of

14 kg, whilst the figure for the lowlands reflects production from ewes of 70 kg LW stocked at 14/ha with a lambing percentage of 180 and lamb carcase weight of 20 kg. Whilst these outputs are lower than the highest that can be obtained from systems involving high rates of fertiliser N, they are higher than those achieved by most producers. Table 7 illustrates that grass–clover swards without fertiliser-N at North Wyke have supported higher stocking weights than those of the top third of lowland producers in South-West England participating in the Meat and Livestock Commission's Flockplan recording scheme, and at the same time a much higher percentage of the lambs were finished from grazing. The challenge is now to develop clover-based systems of production on farms.

Table 7. Sheep live weight during the grazing season, 1985

	Average live weight carried (kg/ha)	Kg N per ha	% Lambs finished
Grass–clover rotational	1508	0	85
Grass + N (top one third)	1349	165	50
Grass + N (average)	1137	152	48

(Data from Meat and Livestock Commission, 1986)

PROBLEMS AND FUTURE DEVELOPMENTS

A major factor limiting the wider use of white clover based systems is their apparent unpredictability. The contribution of white clover on farms is often low and highly variable. Consequently, increased effort is now being devoted to elucidate the reasons for this, and to improve the reliability of white clover, at WPBS, AGRI and elsewhere.

Problems associated with white clover were discussed in detail by Morrison *et al.* (1985). Although a wide range of pests and diseases can attack white clover, the incidence varying greatly from year to year, the economics of controlling the main pests and diseases has not been fully investigated. *Sclerotinia* (clover rot) is the main disease and is widespread in the south and east. Resistant varieties should be grown where the disease occurs. Bloat is uncommon with sheep and there are no recorded instances of oestrogens, which are contained in diseased leaves of white clover, affecting the reproductive performance of ewes.

The potential for improving the reliability of white clover by breeding has been highlighted at WPBS (Davies and Evans, 1986). Increases of up to 25% in pasture production can be obtained through using more compatible ryegrass and clover varieties in the sward. Since white clover grows more slowly than grass at low temperatures it is at a competitive disadvantage in spring which may result in an unreliable and lower clover contribution later in the year. Promising new material which grows more actively in spring and also gives greater annual production is now under test. A white clover variety with better spring growth would be of immense value to sheep farmers throughout the country.

Between-year variability of white clover means that research and development work should be carried out for a reasonable number of years. Since 1985 and 1986 have been exceptionally good clover years care must be taken in interpretation of results obtained during this period.

REFERENCES

BETTS, J. E., NEWTON, J. E. and WILDE, R. M. (1983) A comparison between ryegrass and ryegrass–white clover for finishing weaned lambs. *Grass and Forage Science,* **38,** 142–143.

CLARK, D. A. and HARRIS, P. S. (1985) Composition of the diet of sheep grazing swards of differing white clover content and spatial distribution. *New Zealand Journal of Agricultural Research,* **28,** 233–240.

COLLINS, D. P. (1985) Beef production from white clover–grass swards. In: *Nutrition, Agronomy and Breeding of White Clover,* pp. 57–66. Workshop at Johnstown Castle, Ireland. Commission of the European Communities.

COWLING, D. W. (1982) Biological nitrogen fixation and grassland production in the United Kingdom. *Philosphical Transactions of The Royal Society, London, B,* **296,** 397–404.

CURLL, M. L. and WILKINS, R. J. (1982) Frequency and severity of defoliation of grass and clover by sheep at different stocking rates. *Grass and Forage Science,* **37,** 291–298.

CURLL, M. L. and WILKINS, R. J. (1985) The effect of cutting for conservation on a grazed perennial ryegrass–white clover pasture. *Grass and Forage Science,* **40,** 19–30.

CURLL, M. L., WILKINS, R. J., SNAYDON, R. W. and SHANMUGALINGHAM, V. S. (1985a) The effects of stocking rate and nitrogen fertilizer on a perennial ryegrass–white clover sward. 1. Sward and sheep performance. *Grass and Forage Science,* **40,** 129–140.

CURLL, M. L., WILKINS, R. J., SNAYDON, R. W. and SHANMUGALINGHAM, V. S. (1985b) The effects of stocking rate and nitrogen fertilizer on a perennial ryegrass–white clover sward. 2. Subsequent sward and sheep performance. *Grass and Forage Science,* **40,** 141–150.

DAVIES, D. A. and EVANS, W. (1986) The role of improved grass and clover varieties in lamb production. *Science and Quality Lamb Production, Agricultural and Food Research Council,* 18–19.

DAVIES, D. A., FOTHERGILL, M. and JONES, D. (1986) Benefit of white clover in ryegrass swards for fattening weaned lambs. *Quality in Agriculture. Agricultural R & D in Wales, Third Conference, Aberystwyth* (in press).

EVANS, D. R. and WILLIAMS, T. A. (1984) Evaluation of white clover varieties in relation to breeding objectives. In: Thomson, D. J. (ed.) *Forage Legumes, Occasional Symposium No. 16, British Grassland Society,* 170–171.

FRAME, J. and NEWBOULD, P. (1985) Herbage production from grass–white clover swards. In: Thomson, D. J. (ed.) *Forage Legumes, Occasional Symposium No. 16, British Grassland Society,* 15–35.

GIBB, M. J. and TREACHER, T. T. (1984) The performance of weaned lambs offered diets containing different proportions of fresh perennial ryegrass and white clover. *Animal Production,* **39,** 413–420.

HOGLUND, J. H., CRUSH, J. R., BROCK, J. L., BALL, R. and CARRON, R. A. (1979) Nitrogen fixation in pasture. XII General Discussion. *New Zealand Journal of Experimental Agriculture,* **7,** 45–51.

MEAT AND LIVESTOCK COMMISSION. (1986) Sheep Improvement Services. *South-West Regional Flockplan Report, 1985,* 16 pp.

MILNE, J. A., HODGSON, J., THOMPSON, R., SOUTER, W. G. and BARTHRAM, G. T. (1982) The diet ingested by sheep grazing swards differing in white clover and perennial ryegrass content. *Grass and Forage Science,* **37,** 209–218.

MORRISON, J., NEWTON, J. E. and SHELDRICK, R. D. (1985) Management and utilization of white clover. *Information Leaflet No. 14, The Animal and Grassland Research Institute,* 17 pp.

MOUSTAPHA, E., BALL, R. and FIELD, T. R. O. (1969) The use of acetylene reduction to study the effect of nitrogen fertilizer and defoliation on nitrogen fixation by field-grown white clover. *New Zealand Journal of Agricultural Research,* **12,** 691–696.

NEWTON, J. E., WILDE, R. M. and BETTS, J. E. (1985) Lamb production from perennial ryegrass and perennial ryegrass–white clover swards using set-stocking or rotational grazing. *Research and Development in Agriculture,* **2,** 1–6.

RYDEN, J. C. (1983) The nitrogen cycle in grassland – a case for studies in grazed pasture. *Annual Report 1982, The Grassland Research Institute,* 150–166.

RYLE, G. J. A., POWELL, C. E. and GORDON, A. J. (1985) Defoliation in white clover: re-growth, photosynthesis and N_2-fixation. *Annals of Botany,* **56,** 9–18.

SCOTTISH AGRICULTURAL COLLEGES. (1983) White clover. *Publication 99,* 11 pp.

SHELDRICK, R. D., LAVENDER, R. H. and PARKINSON, A. E. (1987) The effect of subsequent management on the success of introducing white clover *(Trifolium repens)* to an existing sward. *Grass and Forage Science* (in press).

THOMSON, D. J. (1984) The nutritive value of white clover. In: Thomson, D. J. (ed.) *Forage Legumes, Occasional Symposium No. 16, British Grassland Society,* 78–92.

My Hill Sheep Farming System

J. R. HALL
Inglewood Edge,
Dalston, Carlisle,
Cumbria

My brother and I farm in a family partnership at Eycott Farm, Berrier near Penrith and Inglewood Edge between Penrith and Wigton. The farms are both at 330 m and within the Less Favoured Areas. Rainfall is around 1500 mm and snow is often the main weather problem.

The sheep enterprise is based on 1050 Swaledale ewes at Eycott and 60 North Country Cheviot ewes. About 600 replacement hoggs are kept. The farm overlies limestone and is on the edge of the Lake District National Park with rights on the common fell.

The hoggs are wintered on neighbouring dairy farms and further afield within the county. We feel this expense is justified by superior replacement stocks. The ewes are of a medium type with less bone than the more classic Kirkby Stephen type. Rams are purchased at Troutbeck, Kirkby Stephen or St John's Chapel markets. We use mainly aged rams as we think that the Swaledale does not show many of its best attributes until it is older.

The purpose of the Eycott flock is to provide its own replacements and those for the Inglewood flock where we produce Mule lambs. This flock consists of 685 ewes this year and has been enhanced by 320 ewes and 100 shearlings drafted from Eycott. In addition there are 395 Cheviot and Cheviot × Texel ewes at Inglewood, breeding prime lambs for sale to a family butcher in Carlisle. Around 100 hoggs are kept as replacements giving a total of 2890 breeding sheep on the two farms.

This year the Eycott flock produced 660 ewe lambs, 610 wethers and 90 Cheviot × Texel lambs. The ewes at Inglewood produced 425 Mule ewe lambs, 420 wethers and 480 lambs from the Cheviot × Texel flock.

The sheep year begins with gathering for the late dipping. Ewes are drafted and receive a fluke dose, copper supplement and clostridial vaccine. They are also crutched in preparation for tupping, which starts in mid-November. All ewes are tagged to identify the ram they were mated with, likewise the ewe lambs at birth. Ewes are drawn off as they are raddled to enable the better rams to cover more ewes.

Winter feeding of hay and big bale silage is started when grass is short at the turn of the year. The ewes are scanned and the twin bearing ewes are given extra feeding of a 16% beet pulp and concentrate mix. Single bearers have molasses and all ewes have another fluke dose at this time. Ewes are dosed and vaccinated again pre-lambing. Ewe lambs are ear-marked, tagged, marked, vaccinated etc. and males are castrated and tailed in addition. Ewes and lambs are grazed on silage fields until well into May to give as good a start as possible before following the dry sheep to the hill.

All twins and poorer and late lambers stay on the enclosed land. Shearing takes place in July in time for the early dipping period. Lambs are given copper and trace elements and they return to the fell along with any ewes with twin ewe lambs or remaining lambs from twin wethers which are weaned at this time. All lambs are weaned in September and the ewes go back to the fell once again. Lambs are dosed again and wethers put into silage ground at Inglewood to prepare for sale. At the late dipping ewe lambs are prepared for removal to wintering and a few may be sold.

All wether lambs are sold at Troutbeck market as stores at present as we feel that we should try to improve our lambing percentage rather than try to finish all lambs.

The main structure of our sheep system is the common grazing on the hill. There is no control over the grazing and its quality is moderate with a lot of bracken and very steep land. Silage making is delayed at Eycott to complete the harvest at Inglewood and also give the lambs a better start. Silage is made in big bales for the sheep and self-feed clamps for the cattle. Most hay and the straw is bought in.

The grazing ground over most of the farm receives little fertiliser other than lime because the land is steep, boggy or rocky. The more accessible areas have a spring dressing of 180 kg of 20 : 10 : 10 per hectare and a further 50 kg in late August for tupping.

To raise production, the simplest route would be to have more twins but this would require considerable land improvement, drainage etc., which are severely restricted in the National Park. Income has been improved however by selling surplus ewes from Inglewood at a good premium over cull price for further breeding on better land. The wether lambs have also improved considerably.

The cattle enterprise is based around 400 spring calving cows crossed with Charolais and Blonde d'Aquitaine bulls. Most of the cows are Hereford or Blonde × Friesian. Around 150 cows are at Eycott and the rest, with the replacement heifers, at Inglewood Edge. The cows are fed on self-feed silage and straw in winter on slats or straw bedding. The offspring are also on silage *ad lib* plus up to 2 kg per day 16% protein concentrates. Calves are sold at a year old in Carlisle or Penrith.

As far as the future is concerned, I feel that the hill ewe still provides the hardiness and thrift which is desirable in the intensive lowland flock. There will be changes in the sire breeds of some of the halfbred ewes, and continental ewes will give some advantageous variation on the Mule theme. Leanness and the ability to produce heavier prime lambs will give greater flexibility to specialised producers.

Improvement in the native hill stock will come from improvement in lambing percentages and better milking and carcass quality. Many hill sheep have problems with dentition and health problems are becoming more prominent.

My Upland Sheep System

E. G. OWEN
Fron, Talerddig,
Llanbrynmair, Powys

We run a 122 ha family farm in mid-Wales, lying between 229 and 381 m above sea level. We have around 1520 mm rainfall and the climate is best described as eight months of winter and four months of rain. The soils are mainly mineral with peat on the highest ground.

Approximately 85 ha are down to permanent grass and the remaining 36 ha are rough grazing. We are limited to 24 ha for first cut silage and half this area for a second cut. The middle 20 ha on the farm are very steep but roads were built three years ago to give good access to the top land.

Between 1972 and 1977 nearly 8 ha were reclaimed every year, mainly from heather, which was burned and then rotavated and the land sown to a mixture of perennial ryegrass and wild white clover. All the silage land receives 63 kg of N per ha in mid-March, followed by 126 kg at closing. Slurry and manure are applied in winter. The grazing fields have 88 kg in early April and possibly compound in June.

In some years two bags of 20 : 10 : 10 compound are given in August. One quarter of the fields are analysed every year.

Before improvement the hill only kept 100 ewes, 50 of which were dry. Now it is stocked at 12–15 ewes per ha, with some cattle in addition, during the summer. Growth is good even in dry weather but improved spring production would be a great bonus. Some shelter is now being planted.

The sheep flock comprises 550 ewes, mainly Hardy Specklefaces. We have bred more for size and gone in for condition scoring (thin, fit and fat). The Speckles are crossed with a Blue Faced Leicester ram to produce Welsh Mules. The lambing percentage was particularly high (147%) in 1986. A further 250 ewe hoggs are also kept, 100 Speckles for replacements and 150 Mules. Around 120 Mules are sold as yearlings and all fat lambs are sold dead weight to a local butcher.

The ewes are tupped from 25 October onwards and the hoggs from 10 November. All the hoggs are wintered away on a dairy farm in Clwyd from 10 October to 25 March. The ewes have been scanned for the past two seasons and a steel-framed sheep shed was erected three years ago. All ewes are housed from eight weeks before lambing except for single-bearing pure breds. One group of 40 single-bearing ewes were taken through to a week before lambing this year on silage alone and this practice will be continued.

Of the 532 lambs sold to date, the average carcass weight has been 16.7 kg and nearly all have been in grade 2, 3L and 3H. The main aim is to get as many lambs as possible off in the middle to end of June before the prices fall. Thereafter the objective is to get maximum weight without getting overfat.

The cattle herd consists of 58 suckler cows, mainly Hereford and Friesian with some Welsh Blacks, calving in August and September. Most of the calves are sold in May at 320 kg or over and the remainder in August. After weaning the cows graze on the open hill until 10 days before calving. All are artificially inseminated by nominated Charolais or Limousin (heifers) bulls. Bulling heifers are purchased every September.

My Lowland Sheep System

J. C. SMALES
Thornton,
Berwick-upon-Tweed,
Northumberland

Thornton Farm runs to 243 ha and has been rented by me since 1976, when I took over from my father. It is four miles inland from Berwick, north-facing or flat, with no trees other than round the house. It is very windy, prone to hard springs with easterly or northerly weather. Sea mists in summer help to produce some very good wheat yields. The annual rainfall is 580 mm and the land is grade 2 and 3.

In 1976, with three tractormen and one shepherd to occupy during the winter, we tried to develop a more intensive version of my father's beef, sheep and grain system. Money became expensive and cattle difficult to make money from. Two tractormen retired and we slowly turned to a system based on wheat and sheep. This has been tuned and developed and for the last three seasons has been based on intensively grazed short-term leys as the breakcrop for wheat.

The flock is changing from Halfbreds to Swaledale bred Mules. We had 830 to the tup this year, three-quarters being Mules. We aim to lamb from 20 March onwards, to stock as intensively as possible, and to sell lambs at 18 kg dead weight plus from mid-June with 50% being sold before weaning in early August and 80% before tupping.

This year we have a new shepherd with modern ideas. We have vasectomised eight rams and crutched the ewes, and we hope to tighten our lambing pattern and make full use of the prolificacy of the Mule ewe. We have also made more use of stubble, particularly peas, to keep ewes leaner.

We sow 32 ha of grass each year, 16 of two year leys sown under barley, grazed in the first year and made into hay in the second. These are a mixture of Morenne, Talbot and Contender diploid perennial ryegrasses, Fantoom, Condessa and Bastion tetraploids with a small amount of Huia white clover. Sixteen ha of one year ley are also sown after winter barley. This is a 50 : 50 mix of RvP and Bartolini Italian ryegrasses. The 32 ha get 63 kg of N in September and are grazed with wormed ewes in October and November. This autumn the undersown grass carried 20–22 ewes per ha for five or six weeks. The newly sown grass carried less than half this amount.

In addition we have 24 ha of permanent pasture, 11 ha are rig and furrow near the steading, the remainder being peat bog or in small paddocks. Our steading, largely built in 1830, is now used for sheep housing in winter and as covered sheep yards in summer.

We house our ewes in pens of 50 from early in the new year until after lambing. Hay is the bulk feed together with 16% crude protein pellets bought in bulk from a local mill. These are fed from a dusting at eight weeks prior to lambing up to a kilogram per day during the last two weeks.

All grass gets liquid compound fertiliser (usually 15 : 45 : 45) in late February or early March. This has no scientific basis but I find it wakens the grass and warns it spring is getting nearer. I now follow T200 to get the date of first nitrogen application. Sixty-three kg go on then with 63 more every 28 days, usually in late March, April, May and June. We usually lay off until September for tupping grass.

The one year leys are stocked first at 16–20 ewes and twins per ha through April into May. At the same time, the maiden two year ley is not as early and is stocked at 10–16 per ha from mid-April. The hay ground and permanent pasture is also stocked at ten per ha. In cold weather, extra pellets or hay can be fed. However, in wet weather, the young grass cannot stand poaching and meadow grasses invade the one year leys.

By early May, the maiden two year ley is beginning to grow fast and the one year ley is running out of steam, so stocking rates are reversed, sixteen upwards per ha on the maiden seeds and sixteen downwards on the one year ley. The young grass, usually three or four fields, are grown as neighbours, so that the shepherd can work sheep back and forward as he thinks the grass is growing.

We normally have our first draw of single lambs in mid-June. We then sell from two fields each week; one drawn for Wooler market on Wednesday and the other for Berwick on Friday. We use the four worm free fields in strict rotation drawing lambs at 40 kg plus initially, then more by hand, less by weight, as the season progresses. We usually sell live and each year we are increasing the number of lambs given creep feed.

At weaning ewes are grazed tightly in one mob and the gimmers are introduced. Six weeks after weaning, the shepherd begins to draft out bad udders and loose mouths. Lean ewes go to fresh grass, better ewes to stubbles, so completing the flock year. Surplus grass, often in August and September, is made into big bale silage to be fed to tail end lambs with a barley supplement.

The farm now has 32 ha coming out of grass into wheat each year as well as 16 ha after peas, giving 49 ha of first wheat, 49 ha of second wheat, 16 ha peas, 16 ha winter barley, 32 ha spring barley and 12 ha oats.

As regards problems we have the national problem of marketing and price. The individual cannot control or influence either. My job is to ensure as good a living as possible for my family and that of my two employees. This is best served by producing as many units as possible, in my case lambs and tonnes of grain. Abortion and worms are the other main worries.

Sheep Production and the Environment

J. W. ALLEN
Cover Point, Stainton,
Penrith, Cumbria*

INTRODUCTION

I have been asked to speak to you on "Sheep Production and the Environment", posing the question how far will the conservation of the countryside, and the enjoyment of it by the public, interfere with the prosperity of sheep farming? Of course the farming of sheep has been part of the agricultural scene in the United Kingdom for centuries. Its profitability has varied through troughs of depression and peaks of prosperity. This was generally related to the need to feed the nation whenever there was a national emergency. On the one hand your product was rejected by the home market if lamb and mutton could be purchased elsewhere, not always cheaper but as a very useful pawn in the game of trade relations and reciprocal trade agreements. Now I believe, for the first time there are people, many of them from all walks of life, who claim that damaging changes to the face of rural Britain are being effected by farmers in pursuit of profit.

For almost half a century now successive Ministers of Agriculture have conducted an annual review with leaders of the industry and the Chancellor of the Exchequer, controlling the purse strings. In consequence the prosperity of the industry is decided for the next twelve months. Today we find that the Minister has also to satisfy the Department of the Environment that none of the measures that he will take to encourage agriculture will have a detrimental effect upon the conservation of the countryside. We are told that we have to be environmentally conscious. Without wishing to belittle these ideals, aren't farmers also conservationists? One wonders what would have been said centuries ago had those people had a say at the time of the enclosure acts which were responsible for the division of the open countryside into a succession of small fields and paddocks resulting in a patchwork effect of what was previously the open countryside. The return to profitability of lowland sheep in the 1980s, with the resultant increase in the sheep population and the establishment of grassland pastures, must delight the hearts of those who crave the green, green grass of England as opposed to the grain monoculture of the previous decade.

FENCING IN THE NATIONAL PARKS

Where there are sheep there must be adequate fences to control them. There is no doubt that this is going to be a point of conflict not only in the hills and uplands

*Former member of the Lake District National Park Special Planning Board.

but on all common land and the areas designated Area of Outstanding Natural Beauty (AONB) and the new denomination Environmentally Sensitive Area (ESA). In addition we have ten National Parks in England, which alone cover 10% of the land surface. Within the National Parks all improvement schemes must be vetted and approved by the Park authority before the Ministry of Agriculture will pay any grant under any scheme. Fencing, to these authorities, is one of the most sensitive aspects of farm improvements.

Hedges are preferred where they will grow. However it is not sufficient for them to offer improved visual amenity, a sanctuary for small birds and various hedgerow plants, they have also to be a stock-proof barrier. What chance is there of establishing such a hedge without double protective fencing for that hedge in its early years? It seems to me that in their ignorance those who devised this scheme felt that half a hedge would be better than no hedge at all yet a hedge for stock-proof purposes is only as good as its weakest point. All farmers will realise the costly claims for damages that can result from straying livestock. The most important need for ordinary sheep management is good fencing, whatever the materials.

In the hills, and particularly upon the high fells, stone walls have been the traditional means of containing and controlling sheep. These are areas which have always kept sheep, nothing else. There is no alternative farming enterprise. They are known as the breeding ground for the sheep flock of England, where a reservoir of pure breeding stock has always been maintained to enable crossing to take place and provide the lowlands with the halfbred flocks, the Mules, the Mashams, the Welsh Halfbred, the Scotch Halfbred and others. This was the reason why, in 1947, the hill sheep subsidy was first introduced. It was envisaged, with a great deal of foresight, that many of the pure breeds would be crossed for purposes of greater prosperity and greater income. It was found necessary to place a subsidy on the pure bred animal. Since the sheep subsidy days we have moved into HLCAs and these have spread much further down the hill and no longer can they be said to be encouraging the maintenance of the pure breeds. I wonder if there isn't a day coming when we have got to face up to the fact that there have got to be two types of subsidy: the social one, which encourages a man to remain in the hill areas and to farm the land, to play his part as he has been described as architect of the scenery and for the sheep to play their part as the lawn mowers of the countryside: and the production subsidy, that it no doubt is on the lower hills, the uplands and even lower down still.

OVERSTOCKING IN THE HILLS

In the opinion of the conservation lobby, farmers in these high hill areas are guilty of overstocking in pursuit of more headage payment resulting in deterioration of the herbage and the consequent threat to many rare wild plants. I know a number of long standing hill sheep men who share my view that the hill grazings are nothing like as good as they used to be, fifty, twenty-five or even ten years ago, and the grazings do give the appearance of overstocking. Yet the same farmers will tell you that any increase in stocking has been achieved by the improvement of the in-bye land and increased supplementary feeding during the winter months, neither of which place any extra burden on the hill itself. Consequently these same farmers ask the question "Is there some other factor giving the same result?" Is it the cumulative result of maximum stocking over a great number of years? It is easy and fashionable today to blame the farmer.

However if the acidity of the atmosphere has killed the fish in the lakes and streams in some of the high rainfall areas in north-west England and southern Scotland, if it has also damaged conifer trees, does it not follow that it will also have increased the acidity of the soil resulting in a deterioration of that grazing, suggesting overstocking? Recent reports show that a loch in north-western Scotland, where all fish life had disappeared due to an increase in the acidity of the water, after six months of placing lime on the surrounding land and allowing it to filter back into the water has resulted in a tremendous improvement in the analysis of that water and fish life has rapidly returned. I would suggest that many of our hill grazings, where we are accused of overstocking and overgrazing, are suffering from the same decline in productivity for those reasons.

Invariably, when mentioning acidity of the soil as a cause for the apparent overgrazing an evasive reply is the rule, and after all, if the Russians won't accept responsibility for the damage done by Chernobyl (and if this country and West Germany won't accept responsibility for the acid rain that has affected many of the forests in Scandinavia) what chance has a poor fell farmer of getting any government to listen to his plea? Nevertheless the herbage has the appearance of being overgrazed to a greater or lesser extent. Nature Conservancy observations confirm this.

On land where the under-nourishment of the soil, whatever the reason, cannot be rectified by man and machine in an economic manner, the only answer from the farmer, the conservationist and even the sheep's viewpoint must be controlled grazing. Controlled at an optimum level which will please all the aforementioned parties, and this can only be done to any degree of satisfaction with the aid of fencing. Despite a 70% grant towards the cost of hedges or dry stone walling (as opposed to the 30% in hill areas now granted for post and wire fencing) does anyone in their right mind believe that today's farmers, even if there were a 100% grant on stone walling on the high inaccessible mountain slopes, would concern himself with new dry stone walls. Yet the simple straight forward, easy to erect and effective post and wire fence will in many cases not receive approval from the National Park authority because it interferes with the 'visual amenity' and therefore there is no grant available.

Talking about stone walling reminds me of a true story, and this has been handed down from my grandfather and father. Grandfather got the story from the men involved, concerning a wall along a ridge between 500 and 650 m above sea level. It was built between 1830 and 1850 and two young men walked six miles each morning over the Lakeland hills to work and back home each night, leaving home at 4 am and returning at 10 pm. This was done six days a week and they were contracted to quarry, carry and build a rood a day – seven yards. For this they were paid 3s 6d each per day so the week's wage was twenty-one shillings – big money in those days for two strong, healthy lads who today, I suppose, would be motorway contracting or working on the oil rigs to reap similar financial rewards. But who is going to rebuild those walls today, let alone erect new ones?

I had an insight into the ESA areas which are expected to be designated by the end of 1986 and in operation in the spring of 1987. They have exactly the same ideas for fences, drainage, etc. There will be "positive" conservation rather than just saying "no" in the National Parks. What has happened to us in the National Parks, with the Lake District in particular, I feel sure is going to affect many other people as well. The simple, straightforward answer is to erect a post and wire fence. I say to these people "You cannot both have your cake and eat it". If the desire is the limiting and control of stocking rates on these open fells then there will have to be assistance with the best and cheapest form of fencing in order to achieve this goal. It is a fundamental conservation matter vital to achieve their aims if they would but see it. It is also a sheep farmer's necessity.

FOOTPATHS IN A NATIONAL PARK

The Lake District is the largest National Park, attracting by far the most visitors. The latest count was 13½ million in the year. These people come to run, walk, climb, fish, watch the birds, study wildlife, swim, sail, ski on land, ski on water and enjoy numerous other pursuits, geographical, geological, hang-gliding, or just to do nothing but enjoy the scenery and, hopefully, the weather. They all expect access to every location that they wish for all these pursuits. This means that all existing footpaths have been opened up. Some have never been used for years but they are now signposted with gates and stiles put in working order. Many new paths have been created. We in the National Park have been extremely fortunate in that the park Authority, through its upland management, have both done the work and borne the cost of this huge operation. However, there are as many public footpaths, as well as bridleways, outside the area of the National Park and these will affect many, if not all, of you to a greater or lesser extent.

There are some extremely vigilant organisations led by the Ramblers Association, who seem to take delight in discovering public footpaths which have been closed for years and having them opened up to the public at large whether they lead anywhere interesting or not. As one who has lived all his life on a farm with 20 miles of public footpaths and an estimate of 100,000 pairs of feet using it to some extent or other, I feel I can speak with some experience of public access. I don't, nor did I ever, begrudge these people their rights or wish to deny them their enjoyment but quite obviously the heart of the Lake District has now become an area of recreation firstly, with farming a very poor second. Equally obviously, public access on that scale interfered very much with my farming pattern, making a great deal of extra non-profitable work. Thankless, repetitive tasks of repair and repair again. It was of no avail to inform people who were trespassing that a public footpath entitles you to walk in single file bearing your normal possessions; or take up your dog and walk. Increasing public access to the countryside as a whole, not just within the National Park, will place an extra burden on farmers and farming.

It is a problem many of us have learnt to live with and it is much the best and happiest if the rights of way are well signposted and the gates and stiles kept in good order. Then there is a much better chance of the walker keeping his dog on a lead when he is in a field where sheep are grazing. Dogs are by far the biggest menace in sheep country and the cause of much trouble and loss that often does not come to light until long after dog and owner have returned to the city. I remember with envy the pre-War days when if a local person owned a dog that chased sheep, then he took it away and had it destroyed as a matter of honour because that dog was not fit to be in the countryside. Now one has to call in the overworked police, that leads to solicitors and then the court and for the first convicted offence the penalty is "keep your dog under control".

PROBLEMS OF PUBLIC ACCESS

On Easter Sunday a couple of years ago, my son, while on his lambing rounds, found a young lamb badly bitten by a dog. He brought home the ewe and lamb and after giving the lamb the usual jabs for septicaemia and ascertaining that no bones were broken, we decided it was in a state of shock but time might help it to heal. So ewe and lamb were put in a field in front of the house where they could be kept under close observation. The lamb could not stand but we attributed this to shock. It was within 20 yards of a heavily used footpath, and being Easter, there were many people and many dogs passing by. We decided a notice "this lamb has been badly bitten by a dog, please keep yours on a lead" might help to get the message across to the general public.

The next 24 hours were most revealing as to how the public reacts. Of course many were sensible, sympathetic, enquiring, but before noon the local police constable arrived and demanded to see me. He had been advised by someone, not a qualified person, that I was being cruel in keeping this lamb alive. He obviously thought so too. I refused to accept this. I thought it had a 50:50 chance and it was my job to save lambs, not destroy them, and it was not in pain. So he went away feeling and looking thoroughly disgruntled. Later, my wife dealt with a mobile patrol policeman on a huge motorcycle and he came to investigate. I saw him from quite a bit away and made my way home. I wasn't as happy about the lamb myself but this man went away quite happy that I was doing my best, but not before he had been besieged by half a dozen onlookers, who had been hanging about and who were obviously the stirrers who had reported me to the police in the first place.

Next came the Sergeant and he knew a bit about sheep and was quite reasonable and told these people "the farmer is the expert, why don't you leave him alone?". But I had a stroke of luck next, a young fellow was examining the lamb and quite obviously knew what he was doing. He told me he was a vet from the local town who had a day out rock climbing. I had done everything right but the lamb was developing meningitis and would need a three-day course of antibiotic, with only a 50:50 chance of survival at the end of it. So not wishing to waste my ewe I did what any sheep farmer would have done, I fostered another lamb on to it. The orphan lamb was fostered on immediately using the dead lamb's skin, and to my great joy and that of some 20 people who were now watching, the ewe took her new lamb immediately and the lamb went underneath and had a good suckle.

Next day I came home from a lambing round and the local policeman was waiting for me again. He had a message from the Inspector, congratulating me on the way I handled what could have been an awkward situation and the local policeman went away for the second time, feeling very disgruntled. I have told this story at some length because it points out the difficulty in educating the public as to how to behave and what is right and what is wrong.

In the instance I have quoted there were people of all ages, race and colour, people from all walks of life, with all levels of education, different jobs and different backgrounds. Yet because it was happening in front of their very eyes, they were all involved. All had a different idea as to how to handle the problem and certainly none were indifferent. It's easy to say we must educate the public about farming, farmers and about the countryside in general but so many different approaches are needed, almost on an individual basis and in many instances a little knowledge is a dangerous thing for they all interpret it differently.

AFFORESTATION

Before leaving the hills I must say a few words about trees. One of the advantages of being a member of the Lake District Special Planning Board is that I have got an insight into what reasonable and sensible people on the other side are really thinking. That helps you to formulate some idea of what they are going to press for in the years to come.

It has been pointed out that for years now, because no one wished to interfere with food production that the foresters have been seeking acres up in the hills and how southern Scotland has suffered. What a lot of great sheep walks have been taken up there by the Forestry Commission and by the Economic Forestry Group. And yet if you find places where it has been a landlord/tenant, this matter has been resolved with a great deal of satisfaction. Why can't we do that on a much wider basis. Trees were always the landlord's responsibility, they are the landlord's crop and whatever we say about taxation, if it encourages them to go in for more trees, I say it must be a good investment. No farmer can afford to sink his capital into anything that is going to take 40 years before he gets a return. I am now farming under the Lowther Estate and they have been proud foresters for many years. They have good trees. Last February, upon a hill which was about 400 m above sea level and very exposed, I was glad of these trees. I was able to feed my sheep flock and they did extremely well. It was so snug in behind those trees that you felt on some wild days that having fed them you didn't want to turn out and leave them.

I believe many lowland farmers where it is equally exposed, could benefit from trees. I remember some years ago we used to send sheep to Norfolk for the winter and on one occasion they had a cold wind coming from the east. It was something we never experience in our part of the world, we are a bit too far from the east coast, but how they could have done with the protection of trees. You can feed hard in exposed conditions and not get anything like the same results that you can by feeding sheep in comfortable sheltered conditions. If there is one thing I have found that sheep do not like, it is strong winds blowing directly at them.

It has been pointed out too that better trees could be grown and some not very complimentary remarks have been made about the afforestation that has taken place. I would agree that it seems as if some people get hold of a piece of land, sling a fence round it, plant it with trees and then go away and forget about it. I believe that if there was a possibility of landlord/tenant co-operation on this matter then we would get higher quality trees because by their very nature farmers pay almost individual attention to every one instead of just throwing them in in a bulk and hoping for the best.

TAKING LAND OUT OF PRODUCTION

On lowland ground, if it is necessary to take land out of agriculture, a thousand hectares of good lowland must save about 50,000 hectares in the hills in the amount of food that it is going to produce in order to reduce the problem of over-production of all our temperate climatic foods. To take land out of agriculture, and pay farmers a subsidy for doing so, is a short-term effort and not an answer at all. We have got to look at something far more fundamental and long-standing than this.

One other factor to touch upon briefly concerns a recent report which pointed out that some of our streams are flowing full of nitrate. Perhaps sheep are one of the farming enterprises that can manage with less nitrogen. It must be an attraction to the lowland farmer, when he decides to change from arable to grass, that his inputs of costly fertilisers will decrease. A return to grassland farming is bound to meet with the approval of the conservationists but we must be extremely careful and watchful that in pursuit of the beautification of rural England the progress and prosperity of the sheep industry is not unduly interfered with. An industry that falls behind new ideas and change rapidly stagnates. When that happens, the very reverse of the effect desired by the conservationist will be the case. There will soon be evidence of neglect and dilapidation. For I believe a farmer will care for his sheep and the countryside as well, so long as it is a viable proposition. Farmers are the greatest, most knowledgeable and most experienced conservationists of all. Listen to them and the nation need have nothing to fear. Ignore them, and the concept of conservation is doomed before it starts.

WORKSHOP SESSION

Introduction to Workshop Discussions, 'Practical Implications'

J. M. M. MUNRO
Welsh Plant
Breeding Station

This Conference was described in the introductory leaflet as a national forum for farmers, advisers and research workers to discuss the future for sheep production in the UK in view of the foreseeable economic and technological developments. The Organizing Committee was careful in the order of precedence given to the three groups of participants. This workshop, where it is hoped the groups can interact fully, is regarded as the centrepoint of the Conference.

There have been considerable economic and technological developments over the last 10 years. Breeding ewe and shearling numbers in the UK have increased from 13 million to nearly 17 million. Output is approximately £600 million, one-eighth of the total of farm ruminants. About 20 years ago, one observer commented that most of the thinking in hill sheep farming was being carried out by the sheep themselves, but this is no longer the case.

The object of the workshop discussions is to prophesy what the next 10 years will hold in store. Participants in the hill, upland and lowland groups are being asked four main questions:

1. What is the future for sheep production in your sector?
2. What has been the most important development in the last 10 years?
3. What do you think will be the biggest development in the next 10 years?
4. Do farmers see a role for sward height measurement in improving grassland utilisation?

Hill Workshop Report

T. H. McCLELLAND
East of Scotland College
of Agriculture

The response of the Group to the question "was there a future?" was a very definite "yes", with the proviso that it had to be support dependent in order to allow the hills to compete with the more affluent sectors. The Group felt that sheep were being used as an alternative enterprise in the lowlands after other livestock and crop enterprises had run into problems. In the hills and uplands alternatives to sheep were few. The hill cow was traditional, excellent for keeping pasture under control but a lovely way of losing money. It was felt that forestry had little place in the hills. If it was wished to decrease the area of productive agricultural land in the UK then every 100 ha of lowland planted would have an impact 20 or more times greater. Goats were a promising alternative but still had a long way to go in terms of being active competitors to sheep. Perhaps, however, they should be considered as complementary as in many cases they could be added on without paying a great financial penalty. More work was required on goats. Sport, leisure and conservation were all alternatives but it had to be appreciated that they cost money and had to be paid for. Society had to put that value in real and tangible terms.

As far as past developments were concerned it was expected that the HFRO two-pasture system and other ideas would head the list. Would you believe it? The Japanese won again with their motor bikes. Perhaps this reflects on the calibre of today's shepherd and hill farmer. However, all was not lost and it was soon apparent that great changes had taken place in attitudes to management. Sheep were being fed all year round, scanning had come in and was being used well, pasture improvement techniques were being employed together with improved systems for pasture use.

The main future need was cash. The harder the farm the greater the need – lowland farmers should get nothing. If society wanted a managed landscape, if we want infrastructure in these fragile communities then more money is essential. There are signs that society is moving in this direction, certainly it is EEC policy and we are beginning to see some of the benefits.

The Group would like to see reintroduction of the lime subsidy as its removal has been particularly hard on the hills. Breeding acid-tolerant legumes for the hills, quantified breeding criteria for sheep, these are specific proposals. Above all, however, we need security in at least the medium term.

The last question – the use of grass height. This evoked much discussion but it was agreed that it had value in managing improved pasture on the hill farm. It also has an additional value in helping to understand some of the dynamics in mixed hill pastures. More information was required in relation to Bent, Fescue and heather dominant swards.

Upland Workshop Report

W. I. C. DAVIES
Agricultural
Development and
Advisory Service/
Welsh Office
Agriculture Department

Farmers, research workers and advisers all contributed to lively Group discussions on the four main topics. As far as the future was concerned, there was worry about continued expansion in sheep numbers in the lowlands which would inevitably result in reduced prices overall. Many felt that the uplands should try to develop certain sectors of the market, perhaps for larger lambs, or even for organic food. Farmers in the uplands did not use many of the inputs that lowland farmers appeared to throw about. Emphasis certainly had to be on better use of resources, particularly in the utilisation of grass.

The major development over the last 10 years was definitely inwintering of ewes, with the change over from hay to silage conservation also being rated highly. There was greater appreciation of the benefits of hand feeding in improving milk production and lamb performance. Shepherds were also better trained. Clean grazing systems had certainly been of great benefit in parts of the UK but had been taken up less in Wales because of the predominance of sheep and the limited cattle population. Reseeding was also considered important. Above all increasing objectivity was now apparent in sheep farming in the uplands.

The next 10 years were not quite as crystal clear. Research workers and advisers again talked in terms of increasing efficiency while the farmers were more concerned with reducing costs and perhaps making systems simpler. No one development would override all others. Major benefits would be gained from producing grass and clover varieties which grew earlier in spring. Researchers and advisers also felt there was good scope for improving the efficiency of nitrogen use. The use of silage as a buffer feed was not, however, seen as universally applicable. All members of the Group considered that more information on the physiology and ecology of white clover would provide clear guidelines for its management.

Resounding support for the use of sward height as a management tool was again given by the more scientifically minded but many farmers felt there were problems associated with lack of cattle, steeper land etc.

Lowland Workshop Report

C. F. R. SLADE
ADAS National Sheep
Specialist

The Lowland Group was the largest, reflecting the keen interest in developments in this sector. A wide range of opinions was expressed.

It was felt strongly that expansion in the lowlands was going to continue in the future. More market research, however, was required. The right product had to be promoted in the right way at the right price. There was a divergence of views on whether to concentrate on numbers or quality. The members from N. Ireland had a special situation because there is no variable premium only a ewe premium. There were also problems associated with variable quality of lambs from small farms and poor abattoir facilities. All members felt that it was important to keep the variable premium as this kept lamb moving in comparison with the intervention situation with beef. The lowlands certainly had more flexibility than the other sectors to produce lamb throughout the year.

In discussing the last 10 years an interesting range of developments were mentioned. Again the value of sheep housing was stressed. Electric fencing had also been of major benefit on arable farms. Lamb survival techniques had been a key feature and worm control had improved through the use of anthelmintics and clean grazing. Tupping management had improved through better understanding of condition scoring and flushing. Sheep recording was generally applied. On a personal basis, the success of the Border Leicester cross in becoming an almost universal sheep was praised but there are still too many breeds in the UK. Winter feeding and the value of silage and straw was important. More efficient use of resources all the way round, men, land and equipment, was evident.

Over the next 10 years, there was a general feeling that there should be more emphasis on health schemes either Government sponsored or by private contract with local vets – abortion was seen as an increasing problem. Tooth loss was also on the increase, probably as a result of wider use of the Bluefaced Leicester ram. The value of group breeding schemes was accepted but clearer understanding of the genetic objectives were required. Artificial insemination would be more widely used but some felt the techniques needed improving. Breaking the seasonality of lambing was also important in the lowlands. Greater understanding was generally required of production and growth. As far as new markets were concerned, we needed to know about flavour and also whether larger leaner lambs were required for convenience food outlets.

There was general appreciation of Professor Clarkson's comments on the control of parasites. There was a strong feeling that the development of a slow release bolus was important and his approach was universally accepted. Wider use of silage was likely particularly in N. Ireland and more would be used in spring.

The use of pasture height was valuable but more information was required on its role in mixed grazing and cutting situations. Clover was also accepted as having potential but precise systems were still in the distance. Early growth and consistency from year to year were still major problems.

POSTER PAPERS

Using Grass from Irrigated Pasture for Sheep Meat Production in the Ebro Valley (Spain)

A. AMELLA

Instituto de Economia y
Producciones Ganaderas
del Ebro (CSIC-Univ.
Zaragoza) – Miguel
Servet, 177 – 50013
Zaragoza, Spain

INTRODUCTION

Sheep production, based on using poor dry land, fallow areas and stubbles, is an important economic activity in the Ebro valley. Lambs, predominantly of the Aragonesa breed, are fattened on concentrates and cereal straw from 11 to 25 kg live weight. Competition from other EEC countries and the traditional low level of intensification have reduced the economic viability of this system. This study has been carried out to investigate the potential of the Aragonesa breed when fed on irrigated pasture and barley straw, without any concentrate feed.

METHODS

The pasture used in this experiment was sown in October 1981. Four 0.08 ha plots were rotationally grazed every three weeks whilst a similar area (0.32 ha) was used to produce 5 cuts of hay per year. The cut and grazed plots were alternated each year to avoid any build-up of parasites.

Rainfall data for the last thirteen years averaged 330 mm/year with temperatures ranging from 5.6 to 24.5°C. The resulting soil moisture deficit of 470 mm/year was supplemented with 1400 mm of irrigated water per year. The soil was a clay loam with a pH of 8.3 and 27% $CaCO_3$. Annual average vegetation cover between 1984–86 consisted of tall fescue (45%), cocksfoot (25%), perennial ryegrass (15%), red clover (10%) and white clover (5%).

Fertiliser was applied at the rate of 196–94–156 ($N-P_2O_5-K_2O$)/ha on the cut area and 236–102–222/ha on the grazed plots. This was as both artificial fertiliser and farmyard manure. All areas received 65 and 75 kg/ha/year of P and K in January. In addition the cut plots received 30 kg of N/ha after each of the five cuts and the grazed area received 20 kg of N/ha after each of nine grazing periods. The balance of the nutrients was applied as farmyard manure, either by spreading in January on the cut plots, or as dung during grazing on the other plots.

Twenty-four Aragonesa ewes, weighing between 45–50 kg at three years of age in 1986, were divided into two groups to lamb at six-monthly intervals. They were 3-week rotationally grazed from mid-April to November for 6–8 hours per day. From November to April the ewes were continuously grazed over all plots for 2–4 hours/day. The cut hay and barley straw was fed *ad libitum* during housing. The only concentrate given to the ewes was 0.3 kg/ewe/day for the 15 days up to lambing.

Average lamb birth weight was 3.2 kg. The lambs remained with the ewes until at least 15 kg live weight, feeding on the same material as the ewes. At 15 kg the lambs were divided into two equal groups. One group remained with the ewes until slaughter at 23–25 kg (22 weeks) without additional feed. The other group were weaned and fed on concentrates indoors. This group took 16 weeks to reach 25 kg, the required slaughter weight for lambs in the area.

RESULTS

The net yield and quality of the grass produced is shown in Table 1. The intake values shown in Table 2 are quoted per ewe-plus-lamb unit for the time that the lambs remained with the ewes. 1.53/lambs/ewe/year were maintained on grass and barley straw at 35/ha with only the addition of 4.5 kg of barley at lambing. Mean daily live weight gain was 158 g from birth to 12 kg and 111 g from 12–25 kg. The system was able to produce 1300 kg of lamb live weight/ha/year with a gross margin of 315,000 pts/ha/year. This is 60% higher than the gross margin achieved by other irrigated crops in the area using a rotation of lucerne, barley, wheat and grain maize.

Table 1. Three years' mean net yield and quality of the grass

	Grazed	Cut	Total
KgDM/Ha	4,985	5,899	10,884
ME–MJ/Ha	51,346	53,091	104,486
ME–MJ/KgDM	10.3	9.0	9.6
Dig. Prot. Kg/Ha	720	694	1,414
Dig. Prot. gr/KgDM	144	118	130
Crude Prot. Dig. Coef.	0.69	0.79	0.74

Table 2. Three years' mean intake/ewe/day

	gDM	ME–MJ	gDP	gCa	gP
Grazing	584	5.2	85	6	1.4
Hay	469	3.1	44	7	1.5
Barley straw	292	0.6	2	2	0.1
Total	1,345	8.9	131	14	2.0

Supplementation of Silage Based Diets for Lambs

G. BUTLER and
K. A. LAYCOCK
Nutrition Chemistry
Department, Government
Buildings, Kenton Bar,
Newcastle-upon-Tyne

This paper details the results of two trials designed to investigate the effect of supplementary protein on live weight gain in store lambs fed silage based diets.

METHODS

South Country Cheviot lambs (32 kg live weight) were housed off grass in early December, weighed, condition scored and allocated into equal groups of 40. Lambs were offered precision-chopped grass silage plus one of the following supplements:
YEAR 1: 200 lambs, 4 groups with 61 D well made silage and the following daily rations.
Groups A, B and C received 0.3 kg of a barley based mix containing 10% fishmeal X, 10% fishmeal Y and 15% extracted soya bean meal respectively. Group D received 25 g of fishmeal Z. After six weeks on trial the supplement to group C (soya) was increased to 0.45 kg, and 0.4 kg barley was introduced to group D.
YEAR 2: 240 lambs, six groups with 67 D well made silage.
All lambs received 0.3 kg of a barley based mix with varying levels of fishmeal (percentage inclusion of fishmeal in the mix): A. 5%, B. 5% increasing to 10%, C. 5 increasing to 15%, D. 10%, E. 15 decreasing to 5% and F. 15%. The changeover for groups B, C and E occurred five weeks after housing. The first draw of lambs was made after seven weeks. After nine weeks on the trial all remaining lambs were offered 0.45 kg of a 10% fishmeal mix.
  In both years lambs were weighed and condition scored at fortnightly intervals. Lambs were drawn for slaughter at approximately 36 kg and condition score 3.5. Silage intakes were estimated on two occasions.

RESULTS

Silage intakes were similar in both years despite the differences in silage quality. Dry matter intake from silage averaged 0.6 kg per lamb per day.

In year 1 lambs grew at 94, 94, 68 and 49 g/day for groups A–D respectively during the eight weeks on trial. Lamb performance was satisfactory despite the low digestibility of the silage. The growth rates indicate the superiority that fishmeal has over soya as a supplement to silage. They also show no difference between the two types of fishmeal used (Provimi and Chilean). Ration D, the low level of fishmeal only, proved to be a useful holding ration until the barley was introduced in mid-January.

In year 2 lamb growth rate was related to fishmeal level. Lambs receiving the highest level of fishmeal supplementation grew faster and consequently were ready for slaughter at an earlier date. Daily live weight gains (g/day) up to seven weeks on trial were: A, 41; B, 69; C, 69; D, 69; E, 84 and F, 94.

Lambs that received the lowest level of fishmeal initially, did not achieve their growth potential but showed considerable compensatory growth when the amount of supplement was increased from 300 g to 450 g.

A further trial is planned to verify these results.

Flushing of Hill Ewes

M. H. DAVIES
ADAS, Redesdale EHF,
Rochester, Otterburn,
Newcastle-upon-Tyne

INTRODUCTION

The number of lambs reared per ewe is the single most important factor affecting income on hill sheep farms. Nutrition is the key, and better pasture at critical stages in the ewe's production cycle can produce large benefits. The three-year trial reported here set out to quantify the increase in sheep production that can be achieved by providing a higher level of nutrition pre-mating, compared with a traditional hill system.

TREATMENTS AND METHOD

Three groups of ewes were established in mid-October each year and subjected to the following treatments:
    a) Grazed on unimproved hill grazing ("hill").
    b) Grazed on enclosed hill with access to feed blocks ("blocks").
    c) Grazed on hill reseeds ("reseed").
These treatments were maintained from 15 October–10 January, and stocking rates were 1.4, 3.3 and 8.6 ewes/ha for the "hill", "blocks" and "reseed" groups respectively.

Grass resource

The "unimproved hill" was dominated by bent grasses (*Molinia caerulea* and *Nardus stricta*) and offered ewes only a poor level of autumn and winter nutrition. The "enclosed hill" was semi-improved with approximately one-third on a mineral soil supporting a bent/fescue sward (*Agrostis* sp. and *Festuca ovina*), but the remainder similar to the unimproved hill. This area provided the best shelter of all three sites being adjacent to coniferous woodland. The "hill reseeds" were fenced and based on perennial ryegrass, timothy and white clover swards, which received 40 kg/ha nitrogen in mid-August.

Stock

Mature Scottish Blackface ewes (2½–6½ years) were used and the rams (Scottish Blackface in 1981 and 1982, Bluefaced Leicester in 1983) were turned in on 25 November and taken out on 10 January. There were 43, 45 and 73 ewes per treatment in 1981, 1982 and 1983 respectively, but there was no "hill" group in 1983. The ewes were managed as one group, apart from the period 15 October–10

January. Hay and feed blocks were fed to all ewes from early January onwards, with compound feed being introduced in early March some six weeks before lambing. All ewes had access to reseeds during lactation with ewes suckling twin lambs remaining on improved pasture until weaning.

RESULTS

Ewe liveweight and body condition

Ewes on reseeds gained weight in the critical period before tupping, and were heavier and in fitter body condition throughout pregnancy. The actual liveweight change in the six weeks before tupping was −1.6, 0 and +1.5 kg for the "hill", "blocks" and "reseed" ewes (Table 1).

Table 1. Live weight and body condition of ewes (mean of three years)

Date	Live weight (kg)			Condition score (scale 1–5)		
	Hill*	Blocks	Reseed	Hill*	Blocks	Reseed
15 October	59.2	58.6	58.1	2.56	2.53	2.51
3 November	58.8	58.1	58.5	2.68	2.69	2.81
25 November (tupping)	57.6	58.6	59.6	2.47	2.44	2.76
10 January	54.4	55.2	56.6	2.29	2.34	2.76
31 May (marking)	51.5	51.1	52.3	1.81	1.87	1.94
5 August (weaning)	54.1	54.2	54.9	2.18	2.20	2.24

mean of two years only – 1981/82 and 1982/83

Lamb production

The figures in Table 2 show a clear benefit from flushing of 16 and 33 extra lambs born per 100 ewes from the "blocks" and "reseed" groups. The consistent results produced over the three years is spoilt only by the reseed group in 1982–83, where the ram did not work satisfactorily (only 29% of ewes holding to first service). The main effect of flushing as expected was to increase the proportion of multiple births from 16% in the "hill" ewes to 33% and 45% in the "blocks" and "reseed" groups.

Table 2. Lambing performance (lambs born per 100 ewes mated)

Year	Hill	Blocks	Reseed	± SED
1981–82	109	126	151	±11.7
1982–83	109	122	120	±12.3
1983–84	—	127	155	± 9.9
Mean	109	125	142	

An Improved Hill Sheep System

M. H. DAVIES
ADAS, Redesdale EHF,
Rochester, Otterburn,
Newcastle-upon-Tyne

BACKGROUND

A hill land resource at 305 m altitude extending to 122 hectares carried 130 Scottish Blackface ewes in 1969. The vegetation was dominated by bent grasses (*Molinia caerulea* and *Nardus stricta*) on two-thirds of the heft, with heather (*Calluna vulgaris*) on the remaining one-third. The performance of ewes during the two years, 1970–71, was 91% lambs weaned, with lamb weaning weights averaging 29.4 kg. This gave an output per hectare of 31 kg of weaned lamb. The policy in the early 1970s was to boost output by increasing stocking rates, which necessitated supplementary feeding of ewes during the winter. This proved successful to the point where by 1976, ewe numbers had reached 210 and weaned lamb output per hectare had steadily increased to 51 kg. However by the late 1970s, it was becoming apparent that individual ewe performance was deteriorating.

LAND IMPROVEMENT

Some 34 hectares of the *Molinia*-dominated ground had been enclosed in 1970, and had received lime and slag in 1971. It was within this enclosure that a programme of pasture improvement was carried out during the period 1979–1982. Reseeding was carried out on 5, 7 and 11 hectares in September 1979, August 1981 and August 1982 respectively, by direct drilling (Howard Rota-seeder) into the native sward. A combination of cattle grazing and mechanical topping before and after reseeding aided establishment and the swards contained some 30–40% sown species (perennial ryegrass, timothy and white clover) 3–4 years after seeding.

PASTURE UTILISATION

By 1983, 19% of the hill had been reseeded to give one hectare of improved pasture per 10 ewes in the flock. These reseeds have been utilised on the two-pasture system to give ewes access to better grazing at times when the response is likely to be greatest. This means resting reseeds for some 4–6 weeks before flushing (early September–mid October) to allow some herbage accumulation. The ewes then have access to reseeded grass during the flushing (five weeks)

117

and mating (six weeks) periods to ensure ewes are in good and rising body condition as they go to the ram, and to maintain this level of condition for some 3–4 weeks after mating. After early January, ewes are restricted to the unimproved hill, where they receive hay and feed blocks. Lambing takes place in late April on reseeds, which together with adequate late pregnancy feeding (aided by pregnancy scanning), stimulates a good milk supply to initiate good lamb growth rates. Ewes suckling twin lambs get priority, but if possible, and certainly after twin-splitting in early June, all sheep are given access to the better quality reseeded pastures during lactation.

SHEEP PRODUCTION

The flock performance figures in Table 1 show a substantial boost in lamb output per hectare by the mid-1970s, the direct result of increasing flock size. Although ewe performance also increased initially due to better winter feeding, by the late-1970s both weaning percentage and weaning weights were declining. Following reseeding the upturn in individual ewe productivity was becoming apparent by 1982, and in the last two years weaning percentage has averaged 120%. The November live weight of ewes has increased from 51 kg in the period 1977–83, to 56 kg in 1984–85. There has also been a gradual rise in lamb weaning weights since 1982 (apart from 1986, when the late spring and increased numbers of twin lambs depressed this figure). The flock output in the two years 1985–86 is twice that obtained in the "base line" years of 1970–71.

Table 1. Flock performance, 1970–1986

Period	No. ewes to ram	Weaning %	Weaning weight (kg)	Output of weaned lamb (kg)	
				Per 100 ewes	Per hectare
1970–73	155	94	30.0	2826	36.2
1974–77	204	95	32.7	3006	50.0
1978–81	217	92	30.1	2633	46.8
1982–84	230	99	31.7	2918	55.0
1985	236	111	32.5	3258	63.1
1986	241	130	29.8	3322	65.6

ECONOMICS

The gross cost of reseeding in 1979–82 was £4105. The returns from lamb, subsidy, draft ewes and wool in 1985–86 (based on 120% lambs weaned) was £50.46 per ewe, of which £31.52 was from lamb sales. The corresponding costs for these two years totalled £17.95 per ewe, of which winter feed for ewes plus hoggs and fertiliser accounted for £8.50 and £3.26 per ewe respectively. Hence flock margin during 1985–86 was £7803 or £32.57 per ewe.

Intensive Sheep Production on a Dairy Farm

H. HARTLEY[1] and
H. M. EDWARDS[2]
[1]Cumbria College of
Agriculture,
Newton Rigg
[2]ADAS

BACKGROUND

The primary enterprise at the Newton Rigg lowland unit is a herd of 170 dairy cows. It is supported by a flock of 200 Mule ewes which ensure good grassland utilisation. Competition for grazing is reduced by lambing a proportion of the ewes in January and intensive grazing spring lambing ewes. The latter are placed on a second year ley not previously grazed by sheep, stocked at about 25 ewes per hectare with lambs allowed to forward creep. The lambs continue to graze the paddocks after weaning until mid-July when silage aftermaths are available. A lambing percentage of 175% lambs sold supports a gross margin of £42 per ewe and an estimated gross margin per hectare of £635 (1984–85).

THE FARM SYSTEM

Newton Rigg farm has a total of 230 ha in the Eden Valley of Cumbria, it lies at a height of 190 m above sea level and has an annual rainfall of 900 mm. Typically it is 80% grass, mostly leys, which supports 170 pedigree Friesian cows and followers, 60 steers from the dairy herd finished on an 18 month system and 200 breeding Greyface ewes. These, together with finishing 400 purchased store lambs, produce an overall stocking rate of 2.4 grazing livestock units per hectare. The remaining 46 hectares are mainly used for barley with some swedes and potatoes for home consumption. Growing barley gives the opportunity to plough out grassland that is not giving the production required and mixtures sown are predominantly medium term leys based on perennial ryegrass, timothy and white clover, with the proximity of the dairy unit determining either a cutting or grazing bias.

The dairy unit is the main enterprise and grassland management has an emphasis on good summer grazing for the cows and high quality silage for the winter ration. In order to make sufficient silage, about 80 ha are closed in spring for first cut. At this time of the year the sheep are competing for grass.

THE SHEEP FLOCK

The 200 ewes run with the rams in August and are subsequently split into two flocks. Those served, usually 70–80, are managed for January lambing. Relatively high levels of supplementary feed are required for these ewes but all the lambs are sold by mid-May and the ewes are then held tightly in one small area. The 120 remaining ewes are mated in mid-October for traditional March/April lambing. During the autumn all the ewes "clean-up" the grass left by cattle and move freely round the farm to avoid sward damage.

SPRING LAMBING EWES

Subsequent to lambing, the ewes lightly graze the meadows and are then transferred to an area for intensive grazing. Six paddocks are erected in a field that fits the rotation, a whole field or a combination of fields amounting to about five hectares. A second-year ley is usually chosen having been cut for silage the previous year and kept free from sheep over the winter. The lambs creep forward from the ewes through an adjustable creep gate. Supplementary feed is offered initially, the decision when to stop depends on the supply of grass and availability of surplus barley.

The ewes and lambs will go around the paddocks two or three times together before weaning at the end of June. The ewes are removed and the weaned lambs graze the paddocks until second cut silage aftermaths become available. The weaned ewes are stocked tightly on bare pasture with the early lambed ewes.

The initial nitrogen dressing is applied at about T Sum 200 at the rate of 80 kg/ha. As the ewes vacate a paddock it receives a further 40 kg/ha at each occasion. The total amount used in a season will vary between 160 to 200 kg/ha.

FLOCK PERFORMANCE 1984–85

The spring lambing flock of 118 ewes with 206 lambs were placed on 4.3 ha on 26 April at the rate of 27 ewes per hectare. Excluding orphan lambs, the lambing percentage (lambs sold) was 175%. A third of the lambs were finished before weaning on 24 June, and 55% were finished off the paddocks. They averaged 19.0 kg estimated carcass weight, receiving £39.81 each. Supplementary feed amounted to 63 kg per ewe. This produced a gross margin of £42.36 per ewe and £635 per hectare allowing for an overall stocking rate of 15 ewes per hectare.

CONCLUSIONS

The system of splitting the flock into two lambing periods allows control of the ewes in the early part of the grass-growing season. There is extra work for the shepherd but it does give the opportunity to confine the ewes to small fields and release grass for the more profitable dairy cows. It is recognised that the ewes are taking a significant amount of grass in the pre-lambing period. To this end, a shed is to be adapted to house the flock from early January to lambing. This will require additional silage but this will be more than offset by the value of earlier grass growth and higher yields of silage. It will also allow for some flock expansion.

The Effects of Stocking Rate, Nitrogen Use, Lamb:Ewe Ratio and Ewe Genotype on Output of Ewe and Output per Hectare

T. J. MAXWELL,
A. R. SIBBALD,
J. R. JONES and
E. JAMES
Hill Farming Research
Organisation, Bush
Estate, Penicuik,
Midlothian EH26 0PY
and Welsh Plant
Breeding, Plas
Gogerddan, Aberystwyth,
Dyfed, Wales

INTRODUCTION AND METHOD

An experiment on upland sown pastures investigated the performance and output from Becon Cheviot (C) and Beulah (B) ewes at lamb to ewe ratios of 1.2 ($C_{1.2}$ and $B_{1.2}$) and 1.5 ($B_{1.5}$), stocking rates of 20 (S_{20}) and 12 (S_{12}) ewes per hectare at two levels of nitrogen, 200 kg/ha/annum (N_{200}) and 100 kg/ha/annum (N_{100}) giving four treatments in all viz. $S_{20}N_{200}C_{1.2}$, $S_{20}N_{200}B_{1.2}$, $S_{20}N_{200}B_{1.5}$ and $S_{12}N_{100}C_{1.2}$, each treatment being replicated three times.

During the grazing season the swards on all treatments were managed to maintain sward height between 3.75 cm and 5.25 cm from the beginning of the experiment in early May until weaning. This was achieved by closing surplus areas for conservation.

The Brecon Cheviot ewe is commonly used in the utilisation of the common hill grazings of South Wales but it is also used in the utilisation of potentially highly productive sown upland pastures adjoining these hill areas. Output from these ewes is high in relation to lamb growth and in terms of output per unit area the use of the Brecon Cheviot is probably more compatible with the operation of extensive low cost systems of production. Smaller farms require to generate income from more intensive use of sown pastures and high levels of reproductive performance. The Beulah ewe, which is of similar size to the Cheviot, has the potential for higher levels of reproductive performance (R. G. Gunn – unpublished) particularly when grazed on sown fertilised, upland pastures.

RESULTS

The results (Table 1) show that at the same lamb:ewe ratio the Beulah produced a very similar level of total output of weaned lamb per hectare to that of the Cheviot. Treatment $S_{20}N_{200}B_{1.5}$ produced the highest level of lamb output and $S_{12}N_{100}C_{1.2}$ the lowest. There were no significant differences in lamb weaning weights between treatments despite there being a higher proportion of twin lambs on treatment $S_{20}N_{200}B_{1.5}$. Nor were there any significant differences in lamb growth rates from birth to weaning.

Table 1. Production data

Treatment	$S_{20}N_{200}C_{1.2}$	$S_{20}N_{200}B_{1.2}$	$S_{20}N_{200}B_{1.5}$	$S_{12}N_{100}C_{1.2}$
Weaned lamb (kg per hectare)	630_a	635_a	722_b	398_c
Weaning weight (kg per lamb)	26.1	26.5	24.9	26.8
Lamb growth rate (g per day)	200	210	194	204
Lambs per ewe scanned for following year	1.34_{ab}	1.56_b	1.82_c	1.43_{ab}
Proportion Area conserved	0.20_{ab}	0.29_b	0.15_b	0.52_c

Values with different subscripts are significantly different ($p<0.05$)

The proportion of the area closed for conservation in 1985 for treatment $S_{20}N_{200}C_{1.2}$ was similar to that in 1984 but 0.12 more for treatment $S_{12}N_{100}C_{1.2}$. A higher proportion was closed on treatment $S_{20}N_{200}B_{1.2}$ than on $S_{20}N_{200}C_{1.2}$ and almost twice as much as compared to $S_{20}N_{200}B_{1.5}$. These results suggest that not only does ewe stocking rate and level of N application affect the proportion closed for conservation but the lamb:ewe ratio also affects it, particularly later in the season.

Differences in pre-mating live weight (October 1985) were small but significant, ranging from 46.6 kg for treatment $S_{20}N_{200}C_{1.2}$ to 50.2 kg for treatment $S_{12}N_{100}C_{1.2}$. The Beulah live weights lie between these values but it is clear that the Beulah ewes have a higher potential lambing rate than the Cheviots. The results for the Beulah at the higher lamb:ewe ratio treatment ($S_{20}N_{200}B_{1.5}$), however, may be confounded since a higher proportion of twin-rearing ewes were selected at the outset to create this treatment.

CONCLUSIONS

It can be tentatively concluded after one year of a two to three year study that higher levels of lamb output may be generated from Beulah ewes on sown upland fertilised pastures than from Brecon Cheviot ewes when managed at the same sward height profile throughout the grazing season. However, lamb growth was no different between the two genotypes. Output per unit area reflected differences in stocking rate and lamb:ewe ratio. At the time of writing (Autumn 1986) treatment $S_{12}N_{100}C_{1.2}$ has now been investigated over three successive seasons. It has consistently produced similar levels of lamb output/ha, lamb weaning weights and proportion of winter forage from silage. Though output is relatively low it has been consistent and the treatment has proved to be reliable across a range of seasons with very different amounts of herbage being grown, particularly in spring.

Fertiliser Levels to Maintain a Grass–Clover Sward on Hill Peat

B. G. MERRELL and
P. J. A. WITHERS
ADAS, Redesdale EHF,
Rochester, Otterburn,
Newcastle-upon-Tyne,
and ADAS, Soil Science,
Government Buildings,
Kenton Bar, Newcastle-
upon-Tyne

INTRODUCTION

A hill reseed, unless properly managed and adequately fertilised, will deteriorate over a period of time. A trial was set up in 1978 to determine the inputs of nitrogen (N), phosphorus (P) and potash (K) necessary to maintain a productive ryegrass–clover sward on peat. The results cover a five year period, 1980–84, and show the effect of a range of N, P and K treatments on botanical composition and herbage yield.

MATERIALS AND METHOD

The trial was sited within a 6 ha hill reseed on 20 cm of peat at 260 m altitude. The area had been improved by pioneer cropping with direct drilled turnips for two years before reseeding in 1977. Five tonnes/ha of lime (magnesium limestone) and 175 kg P_2O_5/ha were applied in 1975, and 110 kg N, 55 kg P_2O_5 and 55 kg K_2O/ha were applied in each of the three years 1975–77.

From 1978 to 1984 the N, P and K treatments were factorially combined and applied annually at the following rate per hectare.

$$N0 = Nil \atop N1 = 100 \Big\} \ kg \ N \qquad {P0 = Nil \atop {P1 = 20 \atop P2 = 40}} \Big\} \ kg \ P_2O_5 \qquad {K0 = Nil \atop {K1 = 20 \atop K2 = 40}} \Big\} \ kg \ K_2O$$

Herbage yield was assessed five times annually using animal exclusion cages, the first cut being taken in early June, and then cuts at approximately monthly intervals to the end of October. The 100 kg N/ha was applied as two equal applications, the first in mid-April and the second in early July immediately following the second herbage cut. The P and K treatments were applied each year with the first application of N.

Botanical analyses were carried out in July/August using a point quadrat technique. The reseed has been grazed by sheep and sometimes weaned calves from mid-April to end December each year and has provided an average 391 livestock unit grazing days per hectare.

RESULTS

Botanical composition

The reseed established well (89% sown species, August 1978) but the very hard winter of 1978/79 resulted in extensive winter kill. In 1980 the sward contained 45.0% perennial ryegrass, 30.3% clover, 18.5% meadow grasses (*Poa* spp.) and 6.2% other species and bare ground.

Table 1. Botanical composition of sward July 1984 (% ground cover)

Fertiliser treatment	Perennial ryegrass	White clover	*Poa* spp.	Other species + bare ground
N0	35.2	27.7	28.4	8.7
N1	41.6	17.6	33.7	7.1

Applied N increased the proportion of perennial ryegrass and *Poa* spp. and decreased the clover content of the sward. Applied P and K had no consistent overall effect on sward composition but K showed a tendency to increase clover content in some seasons and where no N was applied.

Table 2. Dry matter yield at each cut, 1980–84 (kg/ha)

Fertiliser treatment	Cut 1 (4 June)	Cut 2 (5 July)	Cut 3 (4 Aug)	Cut 4 (6 Sept)	Cut 5 (29 Oct)	Total
N0	1590	1463	1688	976	487	(SED ± 145.7) 6204
N1	2479	1748	2262	939	487	7915
K0	1838	1426	1870	798	449	(SED ± 178.4) 6381
K1	2235	1677	2015	941	515	7383
K2	2030	1713	2040	1132	498	7414

Without N, total herbage dry matter (DM) yield ranged from 5703 to 7044 kg DM/ha. Applied N significantly increased DM yields at cuts 1, 2 and 3 and in total season yield. Overall yield response ranged from 13.1 to 19.4 kg DM/kg N with a mean response of 17.1 kg DM/kg N. Yield response to the mid April and early July N application averaged 23.48 and 12.22 kg DM/kg N respectively.

Table 3. Mean yield response to nitrogen and potash 1980–84 (kg DM/ha)

		Potash		
Nitrogen	K0	K1	K2	Mean
		(SED ± 252.4)		(SED ± 145.7)
N0	5593	6330	6688	6204
N1	7170	8436	8140	7915
		(SED ± 178.4)		
Mean	6381	7383	7414	7060

Applied K significantly increased DM yield at cuts 1 and 2 and total season yield. The N0K1 and N1K1 treatments produced a yield response of 36.9 and 63.3 kg DM/kg K_2O respectively. The K2 treatment produced no additional yield benefit.

In the context of pioneer cropping applied phosphate had no significant effect on dry matter yield.

Performance of Store Lambs on Autumn Grass

C. F. R. SLADE
ADAS, Woodthorne,
Wolverhampton
WV6 8TQ

INTRODUCTION

In many lowland situations grass is in very short supply in July and August but after autumn rain, 15% to 20% of the total season's growth can take place from late September to early December. Freshly grown autumn grass can have a D value of 67 or better. Apart from exceptional autumn conditions, cows calving from September onwards will normally give better yields and are more easily managed if housed after calving. This leaves a substantial amount of grass that needs to be grazed before "winter kill" has an effect. Sheep are ideal for this purpose.

METHOD

Store lambs have been introduced to Bridgets EHF in Hampshire for the last six years to control surplus autumn perennial ryegrass growth on cow grazing and silage ground. The lambs have been mainly Suffolk crosses but have included Welsh Halfbred and Mule wether lambs. The lambs have mostly come from an upland farm (Liscombe EHF on Exmoor) but have also been purchased from Wilton sheep fair (near Salisbury). The lambs were obtained in early September and sold in January and February. All lambs were drenched on arrival and were also vaccinated for Pasteurella pneumonia. Supplementary hay was offered when grass was covered by snow but was only eaten after approximately three days of continuous snow cover.

Over a period of three years grass plots were used to assess the effect of autumn and winter grazing on spring grass growth and sward quality.

RESULTS

The lambs were small but healthy on arrival. Growth rates on clean perennial ryegrass leys were good. There were small variations between seasons in growth rate but lambs averaged a gain of 8.5 kg live weight in the first three months on the farm (to the end of November) and 6.4 kg live weight in the next two and threequarter months up to the point of slaughter. Killing out percentage averaged 47% but this also varied between batches. The killing out percentage was lowest (43–45%) in lambs slaughtered during periods of snowy weather.

Table 1. Store lamb performance 1979–1985

Starting weight (kg)	29.9
Final weight (kg)	44.8
Carcass weight (kg)	21.0
Killing %	47.0
Weight gains September to end November (kg)	8.5
Weight gains December to sale (kg)	6.4

As a result of the experience gained and the live weights obtained it proved possible to determine an optimum date of sale depending on the starting weight of the store lamb. It was possible to keep lambs on the farm after the optimum date of sale. Extra live weight was gained but there was also an increased risk, especially in Suffolk crosses, that carcases would become too fat.

Table 2. Store lambs – optimum sale date from grass

	Starting date	Starting weight (kg)	Optimum sale date
Short keep	Sept.	33–35	Nov./Dec.
Medium keep	Sept.	30–32	Dec./Jan.
Long keep	Sept.	25–29	Feb./Mar.

Replicated plots were grazed at different months through the autumn and winter and then assessed for grass yield the following spring. Plot yields were taken in the third week of April to equate to cow turnout time and in the third week of May to equate to the time of first cut silage. Plots grazed up to the end of December gave a small increase in yield in April and May. Plots grazed in January and February gave a marked drop in yield in April but on average were no different to control ungrazed plots in May.

Table 3. Store lamb effect on spring grass DM yield

Time of lamb grazing	Plots cut April (cow turnout time)	Plots cut May (first cut silage time)
December	+6%*	+8%
February	−22%	+1%

% difference to ungrazed control plots

130

A new ley was established in late August following a winter barley crop. This ley was grazed in December but with ungrazed plots left as a control. The plots were assessed twelve months after establishment and there was a 22% increase in the number of live tillers of perennial ryegrass per square metre on the grazed area.

Table 4. Benefit to a new ley after lamb grazing (12 months after sowing)

	Grazed in December	Not grazed
Perennial ryegrass % ground cover	83	74
Bare earth % ground cover	17	26
Effect on number of live tillers per m² %	+22	0

CONCLUSIONS

The Pasteurella vaccination and worm drench on arrival proved to be important husbandry points. Store lamb performance on clean perennial ryegrass leys was good with an overall live weight gain of 14.9 kg.

The number of lamb grazing days on established leys averaged 700 per hectare. There were variations between swards but this overall grazing density gave a good live weight gain and also controlled surplus grass growth.

In order to get the best effect from grazing with lambs and yet not affect the yield of spring grass for the dairy herd, the results from the grass plots suggest that cow grazing ground should be grazed before the end of December and silage ground grazed in January and February.

Planned Grazing for the Prolific Ewe Flock

W. M. TEMPEST and
C. M. MINTER
Harper Adams
Agricultural College,
Newport, Salop.

*SUMMARY

The hypothesis is that litters of lambs reared by prolific ewes will not reach slaughter weight off summer grazing. There is therefore no point in lambing them at a conventional time in March. Lambing could be delayed until late April/early May, thus maximising prolificacy from a mid-season mating and enabling accumulation of early season grass growth which will carry a high summer stocking rate to produce a high output of lamb per hectare.

Stocking rate was calculated theoretically using tables to predict grass dry matter production/ha from a knowledge of site class and nitrogen application/ha, and assuming a voluntary grass dry matter intake of 40 g/kg live weight for lactating ewes.

Grass production, ewe condition score and weight change, lamb growth and total lamb live weight produced/ha were recorded.

Over a three year period mean output/ha was 1388, 1430, 1171 kg lamb live weight at mean stocking rates of 1921, 2722 and 3363 kg ewe live weight/ha.

It is therefore concluded that high lamb output/ha from prolific ewes lambing late is possible by planning the stocking rate according to site class, fertiliser use and ewe live weight. The data from this trial suggest that at site class 3, using up to 350 kg N, maximum lamb output (approximately 1.7 t lamb live weight/ha) is achieved at approximately 2400 kg ewe live weight/ha (40 × 60 kg ewes per hectare).

*The full text of this paper was not available at the time of printing.

The Performance of Sheep Flocks on Dairy Farms

G. E. POLLOTT and
A. H. POOLE
Meat and Livestock
Commission, PO Box 44,
Bletchley, Milton Keynes
MK2 2EF and
Milk Marketing Board,
39, Christchurch Road,
Reading, Berkshire
RG2 7AW

INTRODUCTION

The recent imposition of quotas for milk production has prompted dairy farmers to evaluate alternative enterprises with a view to altering the balance of enterprises on their farms. At first glance the establishment of a ewe flock would seem to be an attractive alternative to dairying. This paper presents the results of ewe flocks kept on dairy farms which record with MLC's Flockplan and MMB's Total Farm Business recording schemes. In addition some consideration is given to margins and working capital requirements for several alternative livestock enterprises, and the integration of a ewe flock with the dairy herd is discussed.

RESULTS FROM RECORDED FARMS

The results presented here are from 222 dairy farms recording with either MLC or MMB during 1984/85. Some measures of grassland performance are shown in Table 1 and compared to results from other lowland flocks recording with Flockplan. Both the live weight of stock carried per hectare and the summer stocking rate were higher on dairy farms. However, a higher use of nitrogen was employed per hectare and per ewe. Although this indicates a less efficient use of nitrogen per ewe on dairy farms the increase in summer stocking on dairy farms was higher than expected for a difference of 53 kg N/ha. MLC (1985) suggests a difference of 1.54 ewes/ha in summer stocking rate for this difference in nitrogen use.

The physical performance summarised in Table 2 shows a slightly lower rearing percentage for dairy farms but better lamb sales performance with a higher price per kg and more lambs sold finished. Also a higher proportion of dairy farms used silage as their main source of winter forage.

Table 1. Grassland performance

	Dairy farms	Other lowland farms
Live weight carried (kg/ha)	1,497	1,224
Summer stocking rate (ewes/ha)	14.7	12.5
Nitrogen use (kg/ha)	205	152
(kg/ewe)	14	12

Table 2. Physical performance

	Dairy farms	Other lowland farms
Rearing %	147	149
Lamb sold finished (%)	58	53
Price/kg carcass (£)	2.10	2.06
% of farms feeding silage	47	32

The financial performance in Table 3 demonstrates a higher output and lower level of costs incurred on dairy farms than other lowland sheep flocks. Consequently the gross margin per ewe was higher on dairy farms by £0.74. When coupled with the higher stocking rate a gross margin per hectare of £418 was achieved, £56 higher than other lowland flocks.

Table 3. Financial performance

(£/ewe)	Dairy farms	Other lowland farms
Lamb sales	55.05	54.26
Output	52.54	51.97
Ewe concentrate costs	6.83	7.33
Grass costs	6.95	7.01
Gross margin		
£/ewe	31.72	30.98
£/ha	418	362

OTHER CONSIDERATIONS

Financial

In order to compare the margins and working capital requirements of several alternative livestock enterprises a 20 ha farm was modelled. Three likely alternative beef systems and the current dairy herd were compared to a ewe flock. All results were taken as average for the system from MLC or MMB results. The results in Table 4 assume 100 head on the cereal beef enterprise and that the ewe flock is set up as an alternative to the dairy herd and thus includes the purchase price of the stock in the first year. Clearly the ewe flock provides the lowest margin but the working capital requirement is similar to both dairying and 18-month beef. In the second year this would reduce to about £22,000 for the ewe flock.

Table 4. Comparable margins and working capital requirements

From 20 ha	Gross margin (£)	Peak working capital (£)
Ewe flock	7,598	31,356
Cereal beef	8,000	38,800
Silage beef	18,228	43,028
18 month beef	11,532	29,140
Dairying	18,400	30,000

Practical

It is difficult for a ewe flock to integrate well with the dairy herd as far as grassland management is concerned. If the flock is used as a scavenger behind the dairy herd there is a risk of poor performance by the ewes due to poor nutrition at crucial times in the year. There is also the danger that the ewes may eat into cow grazings or silage crops and both enterprises may suffer as a result.

The labour requirements for both enterprises are similar and in order to get maximum performance out of the sheep it may be necessary to employ additional skilled labour.

There is no doubt that sheep can benefit from techniques often used in dairy herds such as silage feeding, and a high input/high output approach but only if ewe management techniques can be employed to benefit from such methods. One further advantage of sheep on the dairy farm is the use of the flock on the dairy pasture during winter. This can provide good out of season grazing and help prepare the dairy paddocks for the next grazing season.

CONCLUSIONS

Currently ewe flocks are being kept successfully on dairy farms but the change from dairying to sheep is not an easy, low-cost, option. Margins are poorer, capital requirements are high and in order to run a profitable sheep flock a range of new techniques need to be employed in order to make useful returns.

REFERENCES

MLC. (1985) *Sheep Yearbook*. MLC, UK; Milton Keynes.
SPEDDING, A. W. (1984) The value of dairy beef. *Paper presented at MLC/MMB conference*. MLC, UK; Milton Keynes.

The Effect of Fertiliser Inputs to Permanent Pasture and Leys on Sward Production and Sheep Live Weight Gain

M. DALY,
UKF Fertilisers Ltd,
Ince, Chester

BACKGROUND

Annual surveys of fertiliser practice indicate that the amount of fertiliser applied to permanent pasture is approximately half of that applied to leys of two to seven years of age. Large areas of permanent pasture (PP) are capable of improvement without the need to reseed, although farmers consider permanent pastures to be less productive than leys.

A trial was started in 1979 to compare the productivity of an old sward and a reseed under continuous grazing, using four different levels of nitrogen fertiliser. In addition, two paddocks were well fertilised and the live weight of lambs measured over a five year period to compare output from PP and a reseed.

SITE AND TREATMENTS

An old pasture at Montford Bridge, Shropshire was used for this trial. The field was a sandy loam texture soil overlying river terrace alluvium and was of good sward composition (about 25% ryegrass at the start of the trial). Strips of the sward were killed using Paraquat and reseeded using a mixture of S24 early, Talbot intermediate and S23 late perennial ryegrass, Pecora Timothy and Huia and S184 white clover. The spring reseed grew poorly and was redrilled in the autumn of 1979 when a good establishment was obtained.

Nitrogen was applied in six doses giving a total of 0, 180, 360 or 500 kg N/ha (called N_0, N_1, N_2, and N_3). Plots were of 100 m, grazed continuously by sheep and were replicated three times. Two grazing cages per plot were used for herbage yields and grass was cut under the cages about six times per year.

RESULTS

Dry Matter Yield – Figure 1

Over the four years after establishment the yield of herbage of the PP was actually slightly higher than the reseed until levels of nitrogen above 360 kg/ha were exceeded. There was no significant difference between the two swards at any one nitrogen level. The PP responded to 360 kg/ha nitrogen which was the optimum for the site and is about 3–4 times the level applied to these swards in England and Wales.

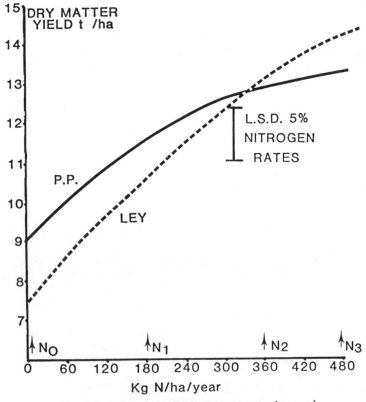

Figure 1. Mean yield 1980–1983 of permanent pasture and reseed.

Herbage Composition – Figure 2

Each autumn the swards were assessed for the species present using a point quadrat method. The ryegrass content is shown in Figure 2 over the duration of the trial. In the PP plots nitrogen has dramatically increased the ryegrass content from 25% at the start of the trial up to 64% by the end of 1983 with 360 kg N/ha and 50% with 180 kg N/ha. In the absence of nitrogen the ryegrass has remained at about 25% throughout the trial. Optimum nitrogen rates have also helped maintain the ryegrass content of the reseed at a uniform level over the four assessment years.

There was little difference between the 360 and 500 kg N/ha rates in terms of changes in ryegrass content over the four years.

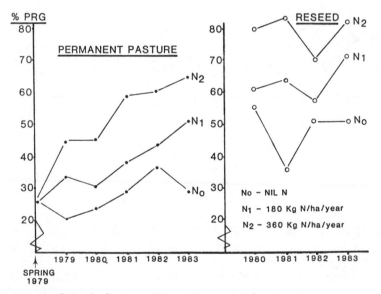

Figure 2. Autumn botanical composition – % perennial ryegrass.

Lamb Live Weight Production Trial – Figure 3

Two paddocks of 0.18 ha were fertilised at the N_2 rate (300–360 kg N/ha). Ewes and lambs were stocked at the same weight initially on the two paddocks, using Suffolk ewes. Stocking rate started at 28½ ewes and 57 lambs/ha in April and

141

EFFICIENT SHEEP PRODUCTION FROM GRASS

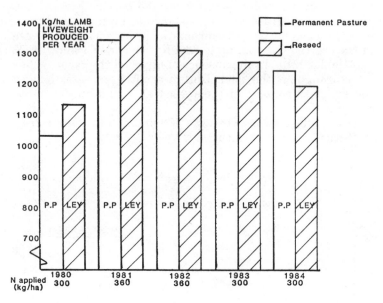

Figure 3. Lamb live weight produced on permanent pasture and reseed.

decreased as the season progressed. All animals were weighed and wormed monthly, and lambs vaccinated. By August most lambs were marketed and removed from the paddocks.

Weaned lambs grazed the paddocks until November when grass growth ceased. No concentrates were fed to the animals. In 1980 the better growth of the reseed enabled more ewes and lambs to be stocked on this paddock, giving about 9% more production in that year. However, over the five years, the mean live weight gain was 1251 kg/ha from the PP and 1254 kg/ha from the reseed.

CONCLUSIONS

Permanent pasture containing some ryegrass will respond to nitrogen rates up to 360 kg/ha. Reseeded grass only outyielded the PP above this level.

Increased N levels raised the ryegrass content of the PP quite dramatically over the four year period from 25% up to 64%.

A five year live weight gain trial gave virtually no difference in lamb produced between well fertilised PP and reseeded paddocks (300–360 kg N/ha applied per year).

Well fertilised and managed PP containing a nucleus of useful species can be as productive as leys for animal output and the reseeding cost is not justified in these circumstances.

Effect of Part-time Grazing on the Performance of Dry Ewes

D. M. B. CHESTNUTT
Agricultural Research
Institute of Northern
Ireland, Hillsborough,
Co. Down BT26 6DR

METHODS

In 1985 and 1986 fifty-six dry Greyface ewes were allocated to 24 hour (full-time) or six hour (part-time) daily grazing at each of two initial stocking rates of 59 and 79 ewes/ha. Treatments were replicated twice (six or eight ewes per plot) in 1985 and four times (three or four ewes per divided plot) in 1986. Part-time grazers had access to pasture between 09.30 and 15.30 hours. On 28 August 1985 stocking rates were altered to 30 and 40 ewes/ha and on 13 August 1986 to 39 and 59 ewes/ha.

Ewes were allocated to treatments from uniform groups of four on the basis of 24-hour fasted weights. On removal from plots all ewes were weighed after a 24 h fast. Condition scores were assessed at the beginning and end of the grazing period. The percentage of time spent grazing was calculated on the basis of observations at 10 minute intervals during daylight hours. Residual pasture yield was measured by clipping eight 0.1 m² areas per plot to ground level at weekly intervals during 1985 and at monthly intervals during 1986. In addition in 1986 pasture height was recorded at weekly intervals using a swardstick.

RESULTS

The effect of stocking rate and grazing treatment on ewe weight and condition score change over the experiment is shown in Table 1. In 1985 weight loss in ewes was substantial, probably as a result of the very wet weather conditions, particularly in the latter part of the grazing period. In 1986 losses were much lower than in the previous year. In both years stocking rate had a significant effect on live weight and condition loss. At the lower stocking rate in 1986 there was little evidence of weight change though condition score was reduced. Length of grazing time did not significantly affect weight or condition loss in either year, although at the high stocking rate in 1985 the loss was considerably lower under part-time grazing.

Table 1. Effect of grazing time and stocking rate on weight and condition score change in dry ewes

Grazing time (hours/day)	6		24		SE
Initial stocking rate (ewes/ha)	79	59	79	59	
Weight change (g/day) 1985	−175	−122	−248	−129	17.5
1986	− 84	− 9	− 82	− 17	8.4
Condition score change 1985	−0.89	−0.99	−1.40	−0.70	0.129
1986	−0.66	−0.38	−0.68	−0.34	0.058

The effect of grazing time on the residual grass yield in 1985 and 1986 is shown in Figure 1. In line with ewe performance residual yield was consistently higher in 1986 than in 1985. During the early part of the period in each year part-time grazing showed consistently more grass than continuous grazing but towards the end of the period there was evidence of a greater yield of grass under continuous grazing. Height measurements in 1986 (Fig. 2) also showed increased availability of grass under part-time grazing over the early part of the period and a change in

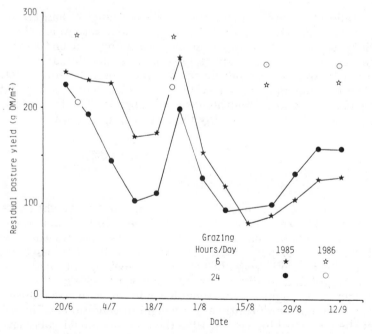

Figure 1. Effect of grazing time on residual pasture yield

the relative positions of yield towards the end of the season. These data suggest a marked change in the nature of the sward over the period. While sward height measurements in 1986 showed a marked reduction from about 9 cm to around 2 cm as the season progressed residual yield changed much less, remaining between 200 and 300 g organic matter per m^2. This indicates that the sward became much more dense as the season progressed.

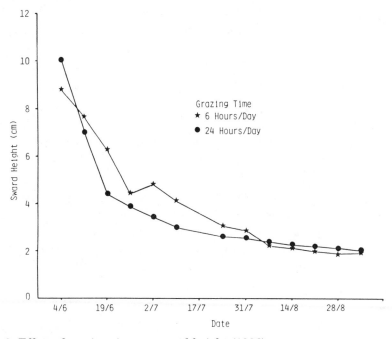

Figure 2. Effect of grazing time on sward height (1986)

Under part-time grazing ewes grazed practically all the time in the three hours after turnout and while there was some relaxation the mean percentage grazing time did not fall below 95% in any hour. Full-time grazers increased their grazing time gradually from dawn and during the common grazing time spent around 80% of the time grazing. They maintained a somewhat lower grazing activity until darkness to give a total grazing time of 10.5 h per day compared with 5.9 h per day for part-time grazers.

Tissue Turnover and Animal Production on Perennial Ryegrass Swards Continuously Stocked by Sheep to Maintain Two Sward Surface Heights

H. CLARK[1],
M. B. ALCOCK and
A. HARVEY[2]
Department of
Agriculture, UCNW,
Bangor
Present addresses:
[1]ADAS, Leamington Spa,
Warwickshire
[2]AGRI, Hurley,
Berkshire

INTRODUCTION

Major advances have been made in our understanding of the flow of material under continuous stocking by sheep (e.g. Bircham, 1981; Grant *et al.*, 1983). Most of this work has been carried out over short periods when sward conditions have been strictly controlled. At Bangor, as part of a four year study examining the influence of perennial ryegrass varieties on animal performance, tissue turnover on continuously stocked swards was monitored over two grazing seasons under a less rigid management policy.

MATERIALS AND METHODS

Perennial ryegrass swards were continuously stocked by ewes and lambs so as to maintain as near as possible two target sward surface heights:– 3.5 cm (HH) and 2.5 cm (LH). Sward height was measured weekly (20 measurements per 0.1 ha plot) using a HFRO swardstick. Tissue turnover was monitored on marked tillers (120–150 per sward height treatment) every 3–4 days within a 12–15 day measurement period. There were 13 measurement periods spread over the two years of the study.

149

RESULTS AND DISCUSSION

In both years a difference of approximately 1 cm was maintained between the HH and the LH swards. There was however a considerable range of sward height values (Table 1) due to the demands of other studies being conducted on the same experiment (e.g. herbage intake) meant that animal numbers could not always be adjusted in line with changes in sward height.

Table 1. Mean and range of sward surface height values (cm), 1983 and 1984

	1983		1984	
	Mean	Range	Mean	Range
HH	3.6	2.6–5.5	3.8	2.3–5.9
LH	2.5	1.9–4.0	2.5	1.3–4.6

Despite the fluctuations in sward conditions the results from this study are in broad agreement with those found under more controlled experiments. The HH sward had the highest rates of growth, senescence and net herbage production (NHP) per tiller although the LH sward had a higher tiller population (Table 2).

The higher tiller population found on the LH sward did not compensate for its lower growth rate per tiller and the HH sward had a higher growth rate per ha. However the HH sward also had a higher rate of loss of material to senescence and so rates of NHP were the same for the two swards (Table 3).

Table 2. Growth, senescence and NHP per tiller (μg/day) and tiller populations/m^2. Average of 1983 and 1984 seasons

	HH	LH	SED
Growth	205.8	155.5	9.4
Senescence	89.2	56.7	7.1
NHP	116.6	98.8	11.2
Tiller Nos.	29,032	36,586	930

As a consequence of the changes in sward height that occurred, higher rates of growth and senescence were not always associated with the HH sward. If either sward was allowed to rise in height, rates of growth were enhanced without a parallel increase in senescence rates. However when they were grazed back down towards their target heights growth rates fell rapidly whilst senescence rates remained relatively unaffected. This is in agreement with the work of Grant *et al.* (1985) which suggests that there is limited scope for increasing NHP by manipulating sward conditions.

Table 3. Growth, senescence and NHP per ha (kg/day). Average of 1983 and 1984 seasons

	HH	LH	SED
Growth	60.8	56.8	3.7
Senescence	25.3	20.1	2.1
NHP	35.5	36.7	3.9

Herbage derived intake studies showed that the amount of material harvested per ha was the same from the two swards (Table 4). Thus the reason why the LH sward had a lower loss of material to senescence was that a greater proportion of the material grown was harvested by the grazing animals. This agrees with results obtained by Parsons *et al.* (1983) using carbon flux measurements. Animals grazing both swards were able to select the vast majority of their diet from the plant parts which have been found to have the highest dry matter digestibilities (Clark, 1985), i.e. the upper leaf fractions present on a tiller.

Table 4. Herbage intake (kg/ha/day) and % of upper leaves in the diet selected. Average of 1983 and 1984

	HH	LH	SED
Intake	44.3	43.1	4.5
% Upper leaves	80.2	79.7	2.0

Estimates of UME output indicated little difference between the sward types. Combined ewe and lamb live weight gain however was higher from the HH sward (Table 5). This was a consequence of a greater proportion of the energy in the herbage consumed on the LH sward being channelled into animal maintenance requirements (Alcock *et al.*, 1984).

Table 5. Total ewe and lamb live weight gain (kg/ha) and UME (GJ/ha). Average of 1983 and 1984 seasons

	HH	LH	SED
Liveweight gain	907	808	37.5
UME	100.6	100.0	2.4

Overall the results of this study add weight to the view that the amount of material which can be harvested from the range of sward conditions that constitute good grazing management is relatively constant. They also indicate that on very short swards, although output per hectare remains high, there is a danger that individual ewe live weight loss and lamb live weight gain can be at a level that is unacceptable in many sheep systems.

REFERENCES

ALCOCK, M. B., HARVEY, A. and CLARK, H. (1985) Sward height for efficiency. *Proceedings of the 2nd Welsh Agricultural Research and Development Conference, Bangor, 21–22.*

BIRCHAM, J. S. (1981) Herbage growth and utilisation under continuous stocking management. *PhD Thesis, University of Edinburgh.*

CLARK, H. (1985) A study of tissue flux in three varieties of perennial ryegrass grazed continuously by sheep. *PhD Thesis, University College of North Wales, Bangor.*

GRANT, S. A., BARTHRAM, G. T., TORVILLE, L., KING, J. and SMITH, H. K. (1983). Sward management, lamina turnover and tiller population density in continuously stocked *Lolium perenne* dominated swards. *Grass and Forage Science,* **38,** 333–344.

GRANT, S. A., KING, K. and BARTHRAM, G. T. (1985) The role of sward adaptations in buffering herbage production responses to management manipulation. *Proceedings of the 16th International Grassland Congress, Japan* (in press).

PARSONS, A. J., LEAFE, E. L., COLLETT, B., PENNING, P. D. and LEWIS, J. (1983) The physiology of grass production under grazing. 2. Photosynthesis, crop growth and animal intake of continuously grazed swards. *Journal of Applied Ecology,* **20,** 127–139.

Improved Grazing Quality for Upland Sheep Systems

J. COOK

ADAS, Ruthin, Clwyd

INTRODUCTION

Availability of spring grass is traditionally low on upland sheep farms. As a result, heavy concentrate feeding is needed during the post lambing period to ensure adequate milk supply for lamb growth.

It is suggested that earlier application of nitrogen will produce high quality grass. This is a much cheaper source of energy and will allow higher stocking rates thus permitting conservation fields to be closed up earlier.

METHOD

The trial was sited on a commercial farm situated at 400 m elevation with an annual rainfall of 1524 mm.

Treatments

1. 60 kg/ha nitrogen applied on 15 March 1985.
2. 60 kg/ha nitrogen applied on 20 April 1985.

Matched groups of ewes with twin lambs were stocked at 12 ewes per hectare on 0.8 ha treatment plots. The plots were rested from 1 January 1985 until the trial started on 23 April 1985. Treatments were replicated three times. Ewes were condition scored and lambs weighed as they were turned onto the plots and again when the trial ended on 28 June 1985.

Sward heights were measured weekly and a target of 4 cm was to be maintained by supplementary feeding or introducing extra ewes on a put and take basis.

Concentrate use, ewe condition, sward heights and lamb daily live weight gains were monitored.

RESULTS

Concentrate use and ewe condition

Feeding was withdrawn from both treatments after three days and was not re-introduced. There was no treatment effect on ewe condition.

Weekly sward height

A sward height of 4 cm was quickly reached on Treatment 1 and was maintained throughout the trial without supplementary feeding by introducing extra ewes. A height of 4 cm was not achieved on Treatment 2 until June 15.

Lamb daily live weight gain

Live weight gains were similar for both treatments (Table 1).

Although there was no significant difference, the live weight gains on Treatment 2 tended to be higher.

Table 1. The effect of N application date on lamb growth rate

	Sex of lamb		
	Female	Male	Mean
Date N applied	Daily live weight gain (g/day) (SED ± 15.62)		(SED ± 11.04)
15 March 1985	221.15	232.71	226.94
20 April 1985	237.67	245.15	241.41
Mean (SED ± 11.04)	229.41	238.94	234.18

CONCLUSIONS

The results suggest that both application dates produced sufficient high quality grass to maintain adequate milk supply and high stocking rates without the need for supplementary feeding or loss in ewe condition. This is a significant contribution to improving the efficiency of upland sheep flocks.

Whilst both treatments produce adequate lamb live weight gains, the trend of higher gains on Treatment 2, where sward height was gradually increasing, confirms the findings of Alcock *et al.* (1985) who reported that higher UME per animal was found in swards increasing in height, due to an increased opportunity for animals to select a higher proportion of the youngest leaf tissue.

REFERENCES

ALCOCK, M. B., HARVEY, A. and CLARK, H. (1985) Sward Height for Efficiency. *Proceedings of the 2nd Welsh Agricultural R & D Conference, Bangor,* 1985, pp. 21–22.

Efficient Management of Upland Swards

M. S. GRIFFITHS and
C. JAMES
Trawsgoed Experimental
Husbandry Farm,
Aberystwyth, Dyfed
SY23 4HT

INTRODUCTION

Previous work has shown that a sward height of 3–5 cm for sheep is the most efficient way of maintaining a balance between new growth and decayed material. An experiment was set up to investigate the effect of sward height on individual lamb performance, live weight gain per hectare and financial returns.

METHODS

A replicated experiment carried out during 1986 using 40 crossbred ewes and their 60 Suffolk-cross lambs to graze a perennial ryegrass sward (*Lolium perenne*) cv Wendy between 24 April and 26 June (weaning) compared animal performance on a common sward of two different heights. Sward height measurements were taken twice weekly with an HFRO swardstick on each of four 0.8 ha plots. Ten ewes and 15 lambs were put onto each plot on 24 April when sward height had reached 4 cm. Two target heights of 4 cm (L) and 6.5 (H) were maintained by closure of part of the area for cattle grazing when the sward height exceeded the target by more than 0.5 cm. Physical data of the ewes and lambs were recorded at 28-day intervals. All plots received 195 kg N/ha in total, applied in three dressings between 14 March and 28 May. Areas on L closed for cattle grazing received an additional 50 kg N/ha at closure.

RESULTS

Mean sward height was 4.5 ± 0.5 cm on treatment L and 5.4 ± 1.1 cm on treatment H. A mean silage yield, after five weeks' growth, of 2.9 t DM/ha was recorded on treatment L using exclusion cages. Ewe grazing days were 926 and 778 per hectare for treatments L and H respectively. Two 14 month old Charolais-cross beef cattle grazed 0.2 ha of L for 28 days following closure from the sheep.

Table 1 shows the mean lamb daily live weight gain on both treatments. Lambs on L gained more slowly than those on H when 0.2 ha of their area was closed for

155

Table 1. Mean lamb growth rate (g/day)

	L	H
22 April–20 May	349	348
20 May –17 June	159	254
17 June –26 June (Weaning)	492	353
22 April–26 June	296	318

cattle grazing on 21 May. Although individual lamb performance was slightly impaired on the shortest sward the mean total production per hectare was increased from 371 kg LWG on H to 463 kg LWG on L between 24 April and 26 June (Table 2). It was estimated that the value of live weight gain was 1.28 times greater for the stock grazing L than for the lambs grazing H.

Table 2. Live weight gain (kg/ha)

	L	H
Lambs	345.4	371.1
Cattle	117.3	—
Total	462.7	371.1
Value (£)	474	371

CONCLUSIONS

Swards grazed at 4 cm lead to reduced individual lamb performance, increased live weight gains per hectare and increased financial margins.

Effect of Pre-mating Sward Height, Ewe Body Condition and Immunisation with Fecundin on Reproductive Performance

R. G. GUNN,
T. J. MAXWELL,
S. M. RHIND and
D. A. SIM
Hill Farming Research
Organisation, Bush
Estate, Penicuik,
Midlothian EH26 0PY
and
J. R. JONES and
E. JAMES
Welsh Plant Breeding
Station, Bronydd Mawr,
Brecon, Powys

INTRODUCTION

This experiment was designed to evaluate the effect of and interactions between immunisation with Fecundin (Coopers Animal Health) and the variation in intake associated with high (H) and low (L) levels of sward height during the four weeks prior to mating of 150 Beulah Speckled Face and 150 Brecon Cheviot ewes in a range of body condition.

Between early August and mid-October, swards were manipulated by varying stocking rate to establish and maintain two different sward height profiles (5–6 cm = H and 2–3 cm = L). The range of body condition in the ewes was also manipulated by differential management on the two sward heights. In mid-September and again in early October, at 8½ and 5½ weeks before a synchronised mating, half the ewes in each breed and condition score and on each pre-treatment sward height were injected with Fecundin. In mid-October, ewes were reallocated by breed, Fecundin treatment, live weight, condition score and

157

Breed	Beulah Speckled Face				Brecon Cheviot			
Sward height	H		L		H		L	
Immunisation	Control	Fecundin	Control	Fecundin	Control	Fecundin	Control	Fecundin
All ewes OR	2.00	2.68	1.38	1.97	1.66	1.91	1.14	1.49
PLR	1.71	1.78	1.13	1.47	1.37	1.33	0.89	1.16
≥2.75+ OR	2.25(4)*	2.80(5)	2.25(4)	1.80(5)	1.83(6)	1.57(7)	1.14(7)	1.71(7)
PLR	2.00	2.40	1.50	1.60	1.50	1.14	0.50	1.43
2.25+ OR /2.50 PLR	2.33(6)	2.20(5)	1.50(8)	2.22(9)	1.83(12)	2.29(7)	1.31(13)	1.56(9)
	1.67	1.50	1.44	1.78	1.58	1.57	1.00	1.11
1.75+ OR /2.00 PLR	2.00(17)	2.74(19)	1.24(17)	1.94(16)	1.54(13)	1.88(16)	1.08(12)	1.33(15)
	1.71	1.74	1.00	1.35	1.15	1.29	1.00	1.13
≤1.50+ OR	1.57(7)	2.80(5)	1.13(8)	1.80(5)	1.25(4)	2.00(5)	0.75(4)	1.50(6)
PLR	1.57	1.67	0.88	1.20	1.25	1.40	1.00	1.00

OR = ovulation rate; PLR = potential lambing rate to first and second mating; *number of ewes in brackets; +condition score at four weeks before mating pre-treatment grouping to the two different sward heights, at 15/ha on the H and 20/ha on the L. The H sward received 50 N kg/ha in mid-September. After mating, all ewes were run on the residual pasture of the H sward fields at 20/ha for four weeks. At return to service or at four weeks after first mating, all ewes were slaughtered for counts of corpora lutea and embryos.

RESULTS

Periodic measurement of herbage mass gave values of about 2200 kg DM/ha at 5–6 cm height, with an October/November mean growth rate of about 23 kg DM/ha/day, and about 650 kg DM/ha at 2–3 cm height, with a mean growth rate of about 20 kg DM/ha/day.

Ewes of both breeds gained weight and condition on the H sward and lost on the L sward until mid-October. Ewes initially on the pre-treatment H sward continued to gain on the treatment H sward over the next four weeks up to mating while those on the treatment L sward lost weight and condition. Ewes initially on the pre-treatment L sward gained substantially on the treatment H sward and also gained slightly on the treatment L sward. After mating, those previously on the treatment L sward gained live weight while those previously on the treatment H sward were either maintained or lost less than 1 kg on average.

A summary of the reproductive performance of ewes from which records were obtainable is shown in the Table. In both breeds, ovulation rate and potential lambing rate were significantly higher on the H sward. Although Fecundin significantly increased ovulation rate in both breeds and on both swards, lower conception rate and higher loss of ova reduced the advantage and only on the L sward was there a significant increase in potential lambing rate. On the H sward, Fecundin did not increase potential lambing rate above that achieved on grass alone. On both swards, control ewes increased in both aspects of reproductive performance with increasing body condition in the Beulah but this trend was not sustained in the fattest Cheviot ewes. Fecundin treatment partially removed the effect of body condition by producing relatively greater ovulation rates in ewes in lower condition but the advantage was not sustained in potential lambing rate, particularly in the Beulah and on the H sward.

Ewe body condition and the level of nutrition associated with premating sward height are therefore important in relation to reproductive performance. Fecundin treatment is only likely to be justified on low sward heights or in ewes in lower body condition.

An Assessment of a System for Maintaining Sward Surface Height on Target under Continuous Stocking with Sheep

C. K. MACKIE,
B. J. KEELING,
M. E. KING and
C. W. WATT
North of Scotland College
of Agriculture, 581 King
Street, Aberdeen
AB9 1UD

INTRODUCTION

Sward surface height (SSH) can be used as a guide for grazing control particularly in continuously stocked systems. It has an influence on structure, growth rate and utilisation of a sward and on the grass intake and performance of individual animals. Recommendations on target SSH for continuously stocked sheep are now available taking account of expected animal performance and time of year (Hodgson *et al.*, 1986).

However little information is available on practical systems for maintaining SSH on target over the grazing season.

MATERIALS AND METHODS

The system used for maintaining SSH on target was a modification of that proposed by Hodgson *et al.* (1986). It was based on using a temporary electric fence (Flexi-net) to adjust the size of the grazing area on a pre-set pattern, taking into account any difference between current and target SSH and any change in SSH over the previous week. The area adjustments are given in Table 1.

The figures in Table 1 are expressed as a percentage of the original area allocated for grazing which allowed the 10% steps to be marked off at the start of the grazing season. Changes in mean SSH over the previous week had to be greater than 0.4 cm to require action.

Table 1. Grazing area adjustments to compensate for SSH changes under continuous stocking

| Current Height | | Change in SSH over previous week | | |
		Decrease	No change	Increase
			%	
	High	0	−10	−20
	On target	+10	0	−10
	Low	+20	+10	0

The areas grazed were under permanent grass (mainly perennial ryegrass) and received a total of 255 kg N/ha applied in four dressings with balancing phosphate and potash. Two ranges of SSH were used, namely 4–6 cm and 6–8 cm with both treatments duplicated. SSH was measured weekly using an HFRO swardstick and 40 readings per area were taken. The temporary fence was moved weekly if required.

A total of 188 Mule ewes with Suffolk-cross lambs born from 1 April were continuously stocked on the areas with the groups balanced for age of ewe and weight, sex and number of lambs. The initial stocking rate was 14.7 ewes with 23.2 lambs per hectare. Live weight of ewes and lambs were recorded fortnightly. The lambs were weaned on 11 August.

RESULTS

Mean SSH and the area grazed by the sheep continuously stocked at the two target SSH ranges are given in Figures 1 and 2 (mean of two replicates). Mean SSH did drift outwith the target ranges rising to a maximum of 6.5 cm in the 4–6 cm target range and to 9.2 cm in the 6–8 cm target range. The drift outwith target was greater, and for a longer period, at the higher range.

In both treatments the area grazed was reduced at one stage to 60% of that initially allocated and on average 7 fence movements were required over the season.

Ewe and lamb performance data are presented in Table 2. Individual lamb performance tended to improve marginally at the higher SSH. Ewe condition score at weaning was satisfactory at both height ranges.

DISCUSSION AND CONCLUSIONS

The trial underlines the difficulties in maintaining SSH within a fairly narrow target range over the grazing season. The uneven and unpredictable rate of grass growth necessitates frequent changes in stocking rate whether by adjusting animal numbers or by, in this case, adjusting the size of the area grazed.

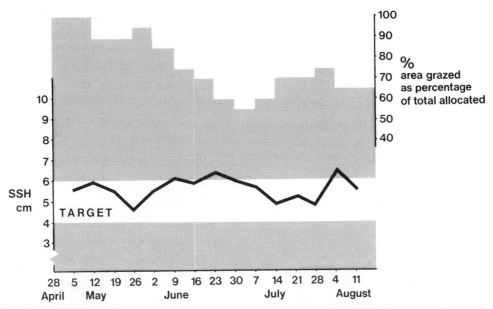

Figure 1. Mean sward surface height (SSH) and area grazed by sheep continuously stocked when target SSH was 4–6 cm.

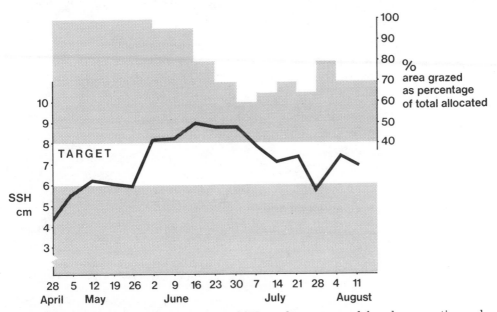

Figure 2. Mean sward surface height (SSH) and area grazed by sheep continuously stocked when target SSH was 6–8 cm.

163

Table 2. Mean liveweights and gains of lambs and condition score of ewes continuously stocked at two ranges of sward surface height

	Lambs			Ewes
Sward surface height	Wt at 20/5	Wt at Weaning	DLWG	Condition score at weaning
	kg	kg	g/d	
4–6 cm	13.7	32.6	250	2.62
6–8 cm	13.4	33.3	273	2.78
SED	0.44	0.60	6.59	0.066

While the system tested did allow SSH to drift outwith target range, the drift was not large and gives some hope for refining the system. The size of the area adjustments need to be increased, particularly during the flush of grass growth, in order to respond more rapidly to changes in SSH between successive measurements.

REFERENCE

HODGSON, J., MACKIE, C. K. and PARKER, J. W. G. (1986) Sward surface heights for efficient grazing. *Grass Farmer*, **24**, 5–10.

Sheep Management on Heather Moorland

J. A. MILNE and
SHEILA A. GRANT
Hill Farming Research
Organisation, Bush
Estate, Penicuik,
Midlothian EH26 0PY

INTRODUCTION

Overall utilisation of the current season's shoots of heather in most sheep production systems on heather moorland is less than 15%. It has been shown that levels of utilisation of 40% in the summer and autumn can be achieved without reducing plant productivity and depressing the intakes of digestible OM from heather by sheep. However, heather provides insufficient nutrients for a breeding ewe in summer and autumn. Attempts to increase utilisation by increasing stock numbers will reduce sheep performance on most heather moorland unless overall diet quality can be improved (see Maxwell *et al.*, 1986). A diet containing above 0.70 of grass, particularly in late summer and the autumn, should provide sufficient nutrients for adequate levels of ewe performance. One means of achieving this is to create a mosaic of sown grass species and heather. Two experiments were conducted to investigate the factors considered likely to influence the proportion of heather in the diet when grass–heather swards are grazed.

METHODS

In Experiment 1 three proportions of grass by area, viz. 0.15, 0.30 and 0.45, were created. The plots were grazed by mature Scottish Blackface wether sheep for 2–4 week periods in May, July and October at stocking rates of approximately 10, 25 and 20 sheep per hectare respectively. Stock were removed from each plot in July and October when 40% heather utilisation was achieved.

In Experiment 2 the same proportion of grass by area (0.30) was used with three herbage masses being compared; these were 450, 900 and 1500 kg DM/ha, which were maintained on the grass area from May until August. A core group of five sheep remained on each plot (0.5 ha) throughout the period with additional sheep being added when necessary to maintain the herbage mass at the desired level. The proportion of heather in the diet was estimated from the concentrations of C_{29}, C_{31} and C_{33} n-alkane in the faeces in relation to the composition of these alkanes in the diet of oesophageal-fistulated sheep grazing the grass or heather areas of the treatment plots. This was a development of the method suggested by Mayes *et al.* (1986).

RESULTS

The proportion of heather in the diet in Experiment 1 increased considerably between May and October (see Table 1). In May the current season's shoots of heather had not started to grow and the unattractiveness of the previous year's growth to the sheep is a likely explanation for the low proportion of heather in the diet. In July herbage mass and allowance of grass per sheep were considerably higher than those in October and this may offer an explanation for the lower proportion of heather in the diet in July. There was no consistent effect of proportion of area as grass on the proportion of heather in the diet with the differences between the treatment areas within a measurement period reflecting herbage mass, or allowance of grass, differences. Further evidence for the effect of herbage mass, or allowance, on the proportion of heather in the diet was obtained in July when an additional set of measurements was made on the 0.45 grass area. An increase in the proportion of heather in the diet from 0.28 ($\pm$0.0266) to 0.52 ($\pm$0.0239) was observed as herbage mass of grass declined from 1100 to 535 kg DM/ha. The proportion, by area, of grass influenced total sheep grazing days and the amount of grass remaining when the 40% target of heather utilisation was achieved.

Table 1. Proportion of heather in diet of sheep grazing grass–heather areas in Experiment 1

	Proportion of grass by area			
	0.15	0.30	0.45	Ave SE
May	0.05	0.14	0.08	0.014
July	0.30	0.22	0.28	0.023
October	0.81	0.64	0.52	0.062

In Experiment 2, apart from a period in early June, there was no evidence of differences in the proportion of heather in the diet between the continuously grazed swards at 450, 900 or 1500 kg DM/ha. The proportion of heather in the diet increased from 10% in early June to 60% at the end of July. A more detailed examination of the results showed that grass intakes declined in June and increased in late July and were positively related to variations in rate of new leaf increment of grass. Heather intakes on the other hand showed an inverse pattern resulting in the increase in the proportion of heather in the diet observed between May and July.

DISCUSSION

During the period from early June, when the growth of current season's shoot starts, until late autumn, the results of Experiment 1 indicate that the proportion of heather in the diet of sheep can be controlled in relation to herbage mass of the associated grass, but that a knowledge of grass growth rate is also required as was illustrated in Experiment 2. At a herbage mass of 800 kg DM/ha or greater, the diet will contain less than 20% heather provided that grass leaf is growing at about 1 cm/day. This will provide a sufficient level of nutrition to support a ewe with a single lamb in later lactation and for the ewe to increase body condition after weaning.

In both experiments 40% utilisation of heather was achieved over the growing season and the heather was ungrazed in winter. By fencing off a part of the moorland to provide a grass–heather mosaic for use in summer and autumn substantial improvement in utilisation of the enclosed heather can be achieved. Correct management of a grass–heather mosaic can lead to predictable levels of sheep performance with additional benefits in terms of delaying ageing of the heather and thus the frequency of burning in the mosaic area.

REFERENCES

MAXWELL, T. J., GRANT, S. A., MILNE, J. A. and SIBBALD, A. R. (1986) Systems of sheep production on heather moorland. In: O'Toole, M. A. (ed.) *Hill Land Symposium, Galway, 1984,* pp 188–211. An Foras Taluntais, Dublin.

MAYES, R. W., LAMB, C. S. and COLGROVE, P. A. (1986) The use of dosed and herbage n-alkanes as markers for the determination of herbage intake. *Journal of Agricultural Science, Cambridge,* **107,** 161–170.

Herbage Production from Different Hill Sward Types Grazed by Sheep

G. E. D. TILEY[1],
T. H. McCLELLAND[2]
and A. WATERHOUSE[3]
[1]The West of Scotland
Agricultural College
Auchincruive, Ayr
[2]Scottish Agricultural
Colleges, Edinburgh
[3]Alpha Centre,
Innovation Park,
University, Stirling

INTRODUCTION

The two-pasture system of grazing has proved to be a simple and straightforward means of improving lamb output from traditionally managed hill sheep farms (Armstrong et al., 1986). This system has been practised for several years at the hill farm of the West of Scotland Agricultural College at Kirkton, West Perthshire (McClelland et al., 1985).

The farm's grazing resource consists of:

- 207 ha   unimproved hill   (H)
- 80 ha   hill improved by lime and phosphate   (HLP)
- 25 ha   enclosed rough grazings improved by controlled grazing and annual fertiliser application   (I)
- 4 ha   permanent pasture   (PP)
- 23 ha   reseeded leys   (L)

Stock presently carried are: 620 Blackface hill ewes, 45 Texel–cross ewes and 22 Hereford-Friesian cows calving in May and June.

The improved rough grazing, permanent and reseeded pastures ('in-bye') have been used strategically with the hill grazings to improve sheep nutrition at mating, lambing and lactation according to the grazing plan outlined in Table 1. Stock carrying capacities achieved on the different sward types are also indicated in this Table. Actual stock numbers and grazing dates are varied annually depending on seasonal grass growth and lambing performance.

The principal objectives in the grazing plan are to graze summer grass growth completely on the in-bye grazings using both sheep and cattle to ensure a high

Table 1. Grazing management plan for Kirkton Hill Farm, with achieved stocking rates per ha

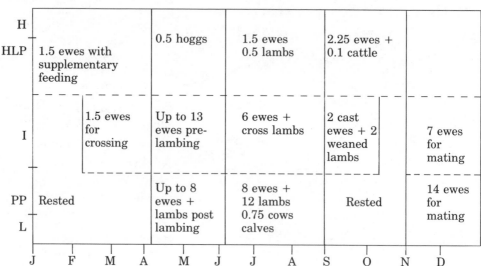

	J	F	M	A	M	J	J	A	S	O	N	D
H / HLP	1.5 ewes with supplementary feeding				0.5 hoggs		1.5 ewes 0.5 lambs		2.25 ewes + 0.1 cattle			
I		1.5 ewes for crossing		Up to 13 ewes pre-lambing			6 ewes + cross lambs		2 cast ewes + 2 weaned lambs		7 ewes for mating	
PP / L	Rested			Up to 8 ewes + lambs post lambing			8 ewes + 12 lambs 0.75 cows calves		Rested		14 ewes for mating	

quality sward of 5–8 cm for the November–December ewe mating and subsequently to achieve maximum utilisation of these improved swards.

Herbage production from the five main sward types has been measured by a movable cage technique during successive seasons since 1981. The results have been used as a guide to stock management and for planning future improvements.

METHODS

The five categories of sward measured were unimproved natural hill (H), natural hill treated with 5 t/ha ground limestone and 0.5 t/ha ground mineral phosphate (HLP), enclosed rough grazings which have received controlled grazing management and annual fertiliser applications for at least 20 years (I), old permanent pasture (PP) and ley reseeded in 1979 (L).

The improved swards (I, PP, L) received annual spring applications of 50 kg N, 25 kg P_2O_5 and 25 kg K_2O per hectare as compound fertiliser. Approximate botanical composition and underlying soil types of each sward type are listed in Table 2. The natural hill comprises a mosaic of *Agrostis–Festuca*, *Festuca–Nardus*, *Juncus* and *Molinia*-dominated communities, according to soil type and drainage.

Current herbage growth was measured under cages at 10 × 3-weekly intervals from 21 April to 27 October each year, using a reciprocating blade mower set to cut at a height of 2.5 cm. After each cut cages were moved to new sampling areas on which the herbage had been pre-trimmed down to sampling height. The sampled area measured 75 × 150 cm, with three cage replicates per sward type.

Table 2. Sward botanical composition and soil type

| Sward type | Species content, September 1981 (% fresh herbage) | | | |
	Perennial ryegrass	White clover	Other species	Soil type
H	0	0	100	Gley/peat
HLP	0	0	100	Gley/peat
I	16	12	72	Brown earth/gley
PP	40	1	59	Alluvium
L	77	1	22	Alluvium

The size of the cage was 90×150 cm at the base, tapering to 75×120 cm at 70 cm height. Construction was of 50×50 mm wire mesh, 3 mm gauge. The fresh herbage was sub–sampled for DM determination, *in vitro* digestibility, nitrogen and mineral (Ca, Mg, P and K) analyses using standard techniques.

RESULTS

DM and DOM production

Annual totals for DM and DOM production from each sward type for the years 1981–1985 are given in Table 3. DM and DOM yield rankings were broadly

Table 3. Annual DM and DOM production, 1981–1985

| Sward type | Annual DM yields, tonnes per ha | | | | | |
	1981	1982	1983	1984	1985	Mean
H	3.90	4.05	3.70	2.79	2.19	3.64
HLP	4.90	3.73	3.56	3.35	3.13	3.74
I	9.11	7.16	7.97	7.06	8.86	7.62
PP	7.78	12.66	9.91	12.16	8.85	10.20
L	11.16	9.65	9.93	11.16	9.39	10.11
SE (difference ±)	0.73	0.77	0.59	0.65	0.78	
	Annual DOM yields, tonnes per ha					
H	1.68	1.62	1.61	1.44	0.95	1.40
HLP	2.14	1.43	1.67	1.76	1.53	1.80
I	4.79	3.41	4.34	4.02	4.65	4.25
PP	4.57	6.78	5.76	7.53	5.03	5.75
L	6.89	5.77	6.04	7.02	5.27	6.15

similar in successive years. Maximum DM yields per 21–day growth period ranged from 0.94 t/ha (H) to 2.65 t/ha (L).

Mean DOM yields per sampling date for the years 1981–1985 are given in Fig. 1. Peak yields for swards L and PP were attained in early June whereas those for I, HLP and H swards occurred three weeks later.

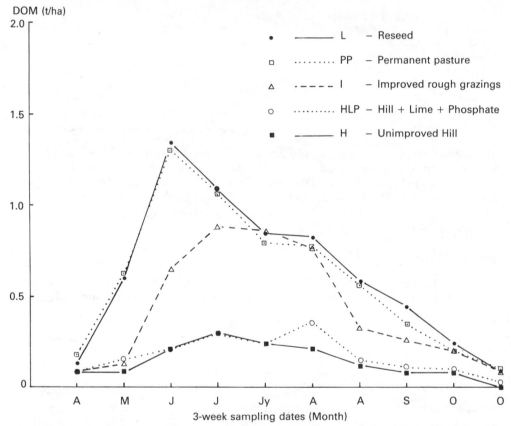

Figure 1. Five-year mean DOM yields from swards sampled at 3-weekly intervals, 21 April–27 October.

Overall five-year mean annual digestibilities were: H, 0.38; HLP, 0.45; I, 0.50; PP, 0.54; L, 0.57. Digestibilities of early and late season growths were markedly reduced by dilution with dead and mature herbage respectively, especially in the hill swards.

Nitrogen and mineral yields

For each sward type annual total yields of nitrogen and the minerals Ca, Mg, P and K for the season 1983 are given in Table 4. Both nitrogen and mineral yields were related generally to the DM production pattern. Small increases in mineral yields were observed in HLP swards compared with unimproved natural hill (H), but yields were lower than from improved swards.

Table 4. Annual DM, nitrogen and mineral yields, 1983

Sward type	DM yield t/ha	Yields, kg/ha				
		N	Ca	Mg	P	K
H	3.7	70	10	6	7	46
HLP	3.6	74	14	7	12	49
I	8.0	276	48	21	34	245
PP	9.9	355	92	54	48	275
L	9.9	353	61	32	52	328
SE (difference ±)	0.6	21	5	3	3	17

DISCUSSION

Annual herbage production from a reseeded ley or well-managed permanent pasture was on average four times higher than from a natural hill sward, and growth continued longer at the end of the grazing season. Herbage digestibility was also higher, especially early in the growing season. Rough grazings, improved over a period of years by controlled grazing and annual application of compound fertiliser, were intermediate in yielding capacity and quality.

There was no yield difference between an ageing reseed and a permanent pasture on similar soil type and under the same management, although digestibility of the permanent pasture was lower. Both these swards contained 40 per cent or more perennial ryegrass. White clover content was only 1 per cent, a feature possibly associated with winter flooding, continuous summer grazing and spring nitrogen usage.

The improved rough grazings were on poorer and more variable soil types, but illustrated the degree of improvement possible over a number of years from enclosure, controlled grazing and fertiliser inputs. The depressed early yields of this pasture type (Fig. 1) were associated with its use as a winter feeding area and thus more intensive grazing.

Application of lime and phosphate to unimproved hill increased mineral contents of herbage, but did not result in any production increase. However, there were indications of more digestible herbage resulting from increased utilisation. This change could be accelerated by the winter feeding (feed supplementation and associated increased grazing) now occurring in this area. The introduction of white clover on the better areas of the HLP sward would capitalise on the previous lime and phosphate inputs through improvement of the sward.

Ideal management, from the point of view of the sward, is constrained by grass deficiency in April and May followed by a surplus in June and July. Conservation as big-bale silage and heavy grazing by cattle and sheep together ensure better utilisation of the summer surplus. The problem of grass shortage in spring is emphasised in late seasons; for example, in 1986 total DM production for the first nine weeks of the growing season was only 34 per cent of the five-year average.

ACKNOWLEDGEMENTS

The assistance of College staff from the Agronomy, Chemistry and Kirkton Farm Departments in sampling, recording and analyses is gratefully acknowledged.

REFERENCES

ARMSTRONG, R. H., EADIE, J. and MAXWELL, T. J. (1986) Hill sheep production: a modified management system in practice. In: O'Toole, M. J. (ed.). *Hill Land Symposium. Proceedings of Conference, Galway, Eire, 1984*, pp. 230–247.

MCCLELLAND, T. H., ARMSTRONG, R. H., THOMPSON, J. R. and POWELL, T. L. (1985) Sheep production systems in the hills. In: Maxwell, T. J. and Gunn, R. G. (eds). *Hill and Upland Livestock Production. Occasional Symposium No. 10, British Society of Animal Production*, pp. 85–94.

Grazing Choices and Hill Management

R. H. ARMSTRONG,
SHEILA A. GRANT and
J. HODGSON
Hill Farming Research
Organisation, Bush
Estate, Penicuik,
Midlothian

All native hill vegetation types contain mixtures of plant species, and most hill grazings are made up of a mosaic of different vegetation types. All grazing animals exercise choice between individual patches of herbage, and between plant species within a patch. Thus, management decisions should take into account the combination of vegetation resources as well as the characteristics of different vegetation types. This paper illustrates two important aspects of variation.

Table 1. Sward and diet composition. Bent–fescue grassland, July 1980 (after Grant et al., 1985)

	Whole sward	Sward surface	Sheep* diets	Cattle† diets
Broad-leaved grass leaf	25.8	28.5	40.4 ± 3.2	40.3 ± 7.1
Fine-leaved grass leaf	25.4	22.1	11.2 ± 2.0	12.1 ± 2.0
Grass flowerhead and stem	8.6	35.4	2.4 ± 0.4	34.3 ± 8.2
Herbs (Dicotyledons)	9.1	2.6	30.3 ± 1.3	0.8 ± 0.3

*means   †means
 5 sheep   4 cows

Within a vegetation type, sheep tend to select groups of plant species in the order herbs > grasses > sedges > dwarf shrubs. They also show a tendency to select broad-leaved grasses in preference to fine-leaved grasses and leaf in preference to stem (Table 1). Thus grazing with sheep alone may lead to deleterious changes in species composition unless grazing is controlled. For example, in one study intensive grazing on a *Molinia*-dominant community led to a marked increase in *Nardus* at the expense of *Molinia* (Figure 1).

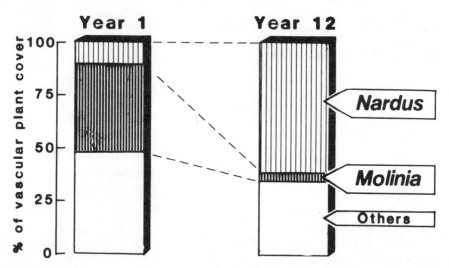

Figure 1. The influence of intensive sheep grazing for 12 years on a *Molinia*-dominant community (after Common, 1986).

Cattle are usually less discriminating than sheep and graze nearer the sward surface; they ingest more flower head and stem than do sheep (Table 1) which gives better control of sward conditions as well as of species composition. However this generalisation does not apply to all vegetation types. On blanket bog and heather moor cattle can be as selective as sheep and risks of poaching and damage to heath species are high (Grant *et al.*, 1987).

The distribution of grazing activity on different vegetation types changes through the year and is strongly influenced by the combination of types on an individual hill (Figure 2). Variation in stocking rate affects grazing pressure on preferred species and vegetation types, the seasonality and level of use of less preferred types and, hence, species composition and community stability.

In current work the relationship between vegetation change and nutrient intake is being investigated on both *Nardus*-dominant and *Molinia*-dominant vegetation. Plots are grazed separately by sheep or cattle and are managed to maintain specified sward conditions. In general, a research approach based on control of sward conditions rather than on stocking rates has led to a better understanding of plant:animal relationships and also allows extrapolation of findings to other sites (Hodgson *et al.*, 1986).

In farming practice, for effective and simple control of grazing, part of the hill with good quality vegetation should be separated from the remaining area by a fence. This allows control of seasonality of use and of stocking rate and, hence, control of vegetation utilisation; it also provides a better opportunity to meet the nutritional needs of animals at critical times of the year. Such grazing control, together with limited reseeding, can have a significant influence on sheep output and financial returns in practice (Armstrong, Eadie and Maxwell, 1984).

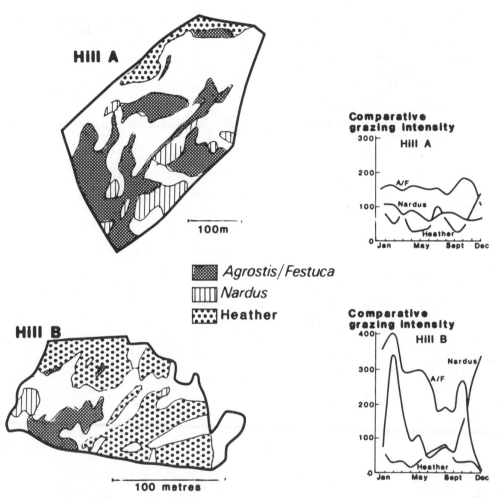

Figure 2. Grazing patterns and the distribution of indigenous plant communities on two hills (after Hunter, 1954; Hunter, 1962).

REFERENCES

ARMSTRONG, R. H., EADIE, J. and MAXWELL, T. J. (1986) Hill sheep production: a modified management system in practice. In: O'Toole, M. (ed.) *Hill Land Symposium, Galway, 1984,* pp. 230–247. An Foras Taluntais; Dublin.

COMMON, T. G. (1986) Pasture improvement studies at Sourhope. *Hill Farming Research Organisation Biennial Report 1984–1985,* pp. 93–99.

GRANT, S. A., SUCKLING, D. E., SMITH, H. K., TORVELL, L., FORBES, T. D. A. and HODGSON, J. (1985) Comparative studies of diet selection by sheep and cattle: The hill grasslands. *Journal of Ecology,* **73,** 987–1004.

GRANT, S. A., TORVELL, L., SMITH, H. K., SUCKLING, D. E., FORBES, T. D. A. and HODGSON, J. (1987) Comparative studies of diet selection by sheep and cattle: Blanket bog and heather moor. *Journal of Ecology,* **75** (in press).

HODGSON, J., GRANT, S. A. and ARMSTRONG, R. H. (1986) Grazing ecology and the management of hill vegetation. *Hill Farming Research Organisation Biennial Report, 1984–1985,* 101–108.

HUNTER, R. F. (1954) The grazing of hill pasture sward types. *Journal of the British Grassland Society,* **9,** 195–208.

HUNTER, R. F. (1962) Hill sheep and their pasture. A study of sheep-grazing in south-east Scotland. *Journal of Ecology,* **50,** 651–680.

Grazing in Broadleaf Upland Woods

F. J. G. MITCHELL
Hill Farming Research
Organisation, Bush
Estate, Penicuik,
Midlothian

SUMMARY*

The shelter and grazing provided by upland broadleaf woods can play an important role in upland agriculture. However, these woods are also prime sites for nature conservation, and overgrazing by large herbivores is normally blamed for the lack of natural tree regeneration. The current conservation response to this is the total exclusion of large herbivores by fencing. It is proposed that a reduction in grazing rather than its cessation may be environmentally a better course of action and would allow some continued use of the woods by stock.

The aim of this project is to identify the impact of controlled grazing on tree regeneration and the ground flora in upland broadleaf woodland on a site in Naddle Low Forest, Haweswater. The site covers 36 ha of a NW–NE facing slope (250–400 m OD). Mixed woodland grades into open *Betula pubescens* wood with rising altitude. Sheep are grazed at three different intensities, designed to remove nominally 60%, 40% and 20% of annual herbage accumulation in fenced plots. Plots at each utilisation level are grazed May–October or November–April in order to assess the effect of seasonality of grazing. Experimental treatments were initiated in May 1986.

The object of this poster presentation is to illustrate the aims of the project and the preliminary evidence on sapling browsing. To put the experimental data in a wider context, it is intended to survey other woods in Cumbria to investigate their regenerative status under varying grazing conditions.

The naturally occurring sapling population show a preponderance of *Sorbus aucuparia*, *Betula pubescens* and *Fraxinus excelsior* with few *Quercus petraea* saplings. To make up for the lack of larger saplings in the wood, 420 saplings of *Quercus petraea*, *Ilex aquifolium*, *Fraxinus excelsior* and *Betula pubescens* were planted in the summer grazing plots. Monitoring on a weekly basis indicates a trend of increased browsing with an increase in grazing intensity, *Fraxinus excelsior* being the most favoured by sheep.

*The full text of this paper can be found in Bell, B. (ed.) *Agriculture and Conservation in the Hills and Uplands*. ITE Symposium, NERC; London.

Tissue Turnover, Diet Selection and Animal Production in Three Varieties of Perennial Ryegrass Continuously Stocked by Sheep

H. CLARK[1],
M. B. ALCOCK and
A. HARVEY[2]
Department of
Agriculture, UCNW,
Bangor
Present Address
[1]ADAS, Leamington Spa,
Warwickshire
[2]AGRI, Hurley,
Berkshire

INTRODUCTION

As part of a long term study examining the influence of perennial ryegrass varieties on animal performance tissue turnover was monitored on individually labelled tillers over two grazing seasons (1983, 1984). The varieties were continuously stocked by ewes and lambs to maintain two different sward surface heights. Since there were no variety sward height interactions the data presented here are averaged over the sward height treatments. A separate paper in this Symposium (Clark *et al.*, 1987) presents the results from the sward height treatments.

MATERIALS AND METHODS

Three late heading perennial ryegrass varieties were used:–
S23   – the first bred late heading perennial ryegrass, now regarded as 'outclassed' by the NIAB.
Melle – a NIAB fully recommended variety, 6% higher yielding than S23 under simulated grazing trials.

Mascot – an Aberystwyth variety whose performance in simulated grazing trials had never been good enough to justify a NIAB recommendation.

The varieties were stocked at two sward heights (3.5 cm and 2.5 cm). The six treatment combinations were arranged in a randomised block design with six replicates. Plot size was 0.1 ha. Tissue turnover was monitored on two of the six blocks on 13 separate periods over the two seasons. Period lengths ranged from 12–15 days and measurements on labelled tillers (25–30 per plot) were made at 3–4 day intervals within each period. Full experimental details have been published elsewhere (Clark, 1985).

RESULTS

Melle had the highest rates of growth, senescence and net herbage production (NHP) per tiller. Mascot had the lowest values for all of these measurements (Table 1).

Table 1. Growth, senescence and NHP per tiller (µg/day). Averaged over the 1983 and 1984 grazing seasons

	S23	Melle	Mascot	SED
Growth	184.9	191.0	166.1	11.6
Senescence	130.5	129.8	128.4	15.5
NHP	110.7	115.2	97.3	13.8

However Mascot had the highest tiller population and so on a unit area basis the difference between it and the other varieties was reduced. The ranking order for NHP was still Melle, S23 and then Mascot.

Table 2. Tiller populations per m^2 and growth, senescence and NHP (kg/ha per day). Average of 1983 and 1984 growing seasons

	S23	Melle	Mascot	SED
Tiller Nos.	31805	31886	34736	1139
Growth	58.8	60.5	57.1	4.5
Senescence	22.4	23.2	22.5	2.6
NHP	36.4	37.3	34.5	4.7

Approximately 80% of the dry matter consumed by animals grazing all three varieties consisted of the two youngest leaves present on a tiller. There were only small differences between the varieties in the dry matter digestibility (DMD) of the diet selected (Table 3).

Table 3. Diet composition (% of upper leaves selected) and digestibility (DMD). Average of 1983 and 1984 grazing seasons

	S23	Melle	Mascot	SED
% leaves and 1 and 2	79.3	81.9	78.7	2.5
DMD	0.78	0.78	0.77	0.05

Animal performance data for the two years of the study reflected the tissue turnover results in that Melle had a small advantage over the other varieties. Mascot however performed better than its herbage production data would have predicted. This is shown in Table 4 which ranks the varieties (S23 = 100) in terms of liveweight gain and utilised metabolisable energy (UME).

Table 4. Rankings of the combined ewe and lamb liveweight gain and UME (S23 = 100). Average of seasonal totals for 1983 and 1984

	S23	Melle	Mascot
Liveweight gain	100	105	101
UME	100	103	99

DISCUSSION

The small advantage that Melle had in growth and NHP was carried through into animal performance and, on the evidence of the two years of this study, NIAB cutting trials can be successful in identifying superior varieties. The performance of Mascot must however be a cause of concern since this is the second occasion upon which animals grazing it have performed better than would have been anticipated from herbage production data (Evans *et al.*, 1980). The most notable feature of the results however is that the differences found here between all three varieties in animal performance are small. This supports those who have argued that the plant breeder has been relatively unsuccessful in improving animal output from grassland (e.g. Lazenby, 1981). This is fully borne out by the results from the full four years of this study when even the small differences in animal performance shown here had disappeared (Alcock and Harvey, unpublished data).

REFERENCES

CLARK, H. (1985) A study of tissue flux in three varieties of perennial ryegrass grazed continuously by sheep. *PhD Thesis, University College of North Wales, Bangor.*

CLARK, H., ALCOCK, M. B. and HARVEY, A. (1986) Tissue turnover and animal production on perennial ryegrass, swards continuously stocked to maintain two sward surface heights. In: Pollott, G. E. (ed.) *Efficient Sheep Production from Grass, British Grassland Society Occasional Symposium No. 21*, 149–152.

EVANS, W. B., MUNROE, J. M. M. and SCURLOCK, R. V. (1980) Comparison of grass varieties under grazing. *Report of the Welsh Plant Breeding Station for 1980*, 63–64.

LAZENBY, A. (1981) British grasslands; past, present and future. *Grass and Forage Science*, **36**, 243–266.

Tissue Fluxes in White Clover Varieties Grown in Swards Continuously Grazed by Sheep

ALISON DAVIES and
D. R. JONES
Welsh Plant Breeding
Station, Plas Gogerddan,
Aberystwyth, Dyfed
SY23 3EB

INTRODUCTION

Relatively little information is available on rates of growth and senescence in white clover plants under continuous grazing managements. Techniques were developed to enable these fluxes to be estimated on grass–white clover plots sown in 1983 on land in the mid-Wales coastal area.

MATERIALS AND METHODS

The experimental design comprised twelve 0.2 ha paddocks, three replicates each of Aurora, Frances, Talbot and Melle perennial ryegrass. Each paddock included plots of three white clover varieties, Huia, Menna and Kent. The paddocks were grazed with varying numbers of Suffolk–cross ewes and lambs in the spring and early summer to maintain a sward height of 4 cm. The target height was later raised to 6 cm after a short rest period (20 June–15 July in 1985; 23 June–17 July in 1986) when lambs were drafted off and before new stock was brought in.

White clover measurements were made over the course of four sampling periods: 1) 8–22 June 1985; 2) 28 August–13 September 1985; 3) 6–20 May 1986 and 4) 23 July–6 August 1986. Collateral ryegrass measurements were made in 1986 only. Field data on white clover included the number of new leaves appearing on marked stolons (about 14 per plot) during the sampling periods. In 1986 numbers of leaves which had been eaten or had died were assessed over the same periods. Counts were made of leaves in four 12.5 × 12.5 cm quadrats per plot, the leaves being removed as they were counted. Numbers of leaves per growing point were obtained from samples (five per plot, normally including about 25 growing points) each eased out with a trowel in such a way as to minimise stolon breakage. From these samples, comparisons were also made of dry weights of matched pairs of eaten and uneaten leaves, the difference being defined as consumable herbage. Growing points per unit area were calculated from numbers of leaves per unit area divided by the corresponding numbers of leaves per growing point. Amounts eaten and lost were assessed from growing points per unit area, numbers of leaves eaten and lost per growing point and weights of consumable leaf eaten or lost at each node.

The amount of new leaf entering the system in perennial ryegrass was calculated as the product of the number of leaves per tiller which appeared during the sampling period, the number of tillers (from four 50 cm cores per plot) and the weight of the first undamaged leaf to emerge during short periods of exclosure (five and ten days). Losses were similarly assessed from the initial weights of lowermost leaves in the open sward and the numbers of bottom leaves lost during the sampling period. Leaf weights in both instances were based on a mean of 15–20 leaves per plot. The amount eaten was taken as the difference between amounts of leaf blade entering and leaving the system.

RESULTS AND DISCUSSION

The typical white clover stolon in a continuously grazed sward carries few green leaves. The number per stolon (including those in which all the leaflets were opening but not open) averaged over the three varieties was 1.40 ± 0.024, 1.32 ± 0.032, 0.91 ± 0.023 and 1.36 ± 0.058 in sampling periods 1 to 4 respectively. Kent retained about one-fifth of a leaf more than Huia; Menna was intermediate. The 1986 data showed that the probability of a leaf (as previously defined) being eaten was highest (about 65%) in the second position on the stolon. Younger leaves in position 1 and older leaves in position 3 were less likely to be eaten (25% and 50% respectively for the mean of periods 3 and 4). The chance of still older leaves being eaten was small.

The number of clover growing points per unit area was substantially higher in summer than in spring. In 1986 numbers per m^2 in Huia, Menna and Kent rose from 1140, 1210 and 3200 ($\pm$ 199) at the end of March to 3050, 2280 and 10,430 ($\pm$ 659) at the end of July. A similar trend was observed in the previous year. The number of ryegrass tillers (counted at samplings 3 and 4 only) was of the order of 12 to 13,000 per m^2.

Throughout the experiment Kent produced consistently and significantly more consumable dry matter per day than Huia or Menna (Table 1), the relative smallness of its leaves being more than compensated by the high population of growing points. The additional production in Kent in 1986 was not at the expense of production by the grass component, which showed no significant differences in relation to clover variety. Production of consumable herbage by the clover component was low in spring and increased in summer; production of ryegrass, on the other hand, fell off. A major influence was a reduction in its rate of leaf appearance from 1.45 ± 0.024 in period 3 to 1.06 ± 0.030 in period 4.

Herbage consumed as a proportion of the herbage on offer in white clover was $92 \pm 0.9\%$ in period 3 and $74 \pm 2.3\%$ in period 4, the lower value reflecting the fact that some of the herbage which had accumulated during the rest period was still being grazed down. (Inclusion of the weight of uneaten petiole would modify these percentages to $72 \pm 0.9\%$ and $56 \pm 1.7\%$). Utilisation of leaf blade in ryegrass was considerably less efficient ($46 \pm 3.2\%$ and $40 \pm 2.0\%$).

Table 1. Rate of production of new consumable herbage in three white clover varieties and in ryegrass (kg/ha/day)

	1985		1986	
	Period 1	Period 2	Period 3	Period 4
Clover variety				
Huia	16.1	13.8	8.0	17.7
Menna	10.3	11.1	7.0	15.8
Kent	22.9	28.5	15.1	48.7
SE ±	1.55	3.52	0.82	2.00
Ryegrass			62.6	32.1
S.E. ±			3.14	1.41

These differences in percentage utilisation between the two species mean that there is more clover in the diet of the sheep than samples of total herbage on offer would indicate. This finding corresponds with results using fistulated animals (Milne *et al.*, 1982; Curll *et al.*, 1985). The relatively high percentage in the diet was associated by the former authors with the high proportion of clover leaf found in the upper sward horizons. It seems clear, in short swards at least, that the favourable position of clover leaves serves to ensure efficient harvesting and minimal wastage.

REFERENCES

CURLL, M. L., WILKINS, R. J., SNAYDON, R. W. and SHANMUGALINGAM, V. S. (1985) The effects of stocking rate and nitrogen fertilizer on a perennial ryegrass–white clover sward. 1. Sward and sheep performance. *Grass and Forage Science,* **40,** 129–140.

MILNE, J. A., HODGSON, J., THOMPSON, R., SOUTER, W. G., BARTHRAM, G. T. (1982) The diet ingested by sheep grazing swards differing in white clover and perennial ryegrass content. *Grass and Forage Science,* **37,** 209–218.

Lamb Production in Spring from a New Early-Flowering Perennial Ryegrass

D. A. DAVIES,
M. FOTHERGILL and
D. JONES
Welsh Plant Breeding
Station, Plas Gogerddan,
Aberystwyth, Dyfed
SY23 3EB, UK

INTRODUCTION

Lack of adequate herbage growth in spring is a major constraint to more efficient sheep production from grass, particularly in the less favoured hill and upland areas. The problem has been accentuated in recent years by a substantial increase in ewe numbers and prolificacy, and with these coinciding with late springs.

Although existing early-flowering perennial ryegrass varieties can provide good growth in spring, their usefulness in the uplands is restricted by poorer persistence and winter hardiness than late-flowering pasture types. A new very early-flowering variety, Aurora, bred at Aberystwyth from plants collected in the Swiss Alps, has been shown to combine good persistence and winter hardiness with high spring production. Therefore, a trial was established in the uplands to assess the animal production potential of Aurora. Results obtained during the first year (1985) were published earlier (Davies *et al.*, 1986). In this paper an examination is made of its potential during the critical spring period in 1985 and 1986.

EXPERIMENTAL METHODS

The trial was established at Bronydd Mawr Research Centre in Powys on Devonian sandstone of the Milford series at 310–363 m above sea level. Details of the centre were published by Munro *et al.* (1985). Individual paddocks (0.4 ha) of three grasses were sown on 15 May 1984 in a randomised-block design with three replicates and two nitrogen treatments. The ryegrass varieties were:

Aurora   – very early-flowering (41–45 days earlier than S.23) based on genotypes of a population collected in the lower Swiss Alps which survived three years' intensive grazing

Aberystwyth S.23 – widely grown late-flowering variety;

Meltra   – a tetraploid late-flowering variety from RvP, Belgium.

Nitrogen fertiliser application on the two N treatments (200 kg N/ha; 75 kg N/ha + S.184 white clover) during the spring period were 84 and 50 kg N/ha on the pure grass and grass–clover swards respectively.

The swards were continuously stocked with Beulah Speckled Face ewes and lambs (lamb:ewe ratio of 1.2 : 1 and 1.5:1 in 1985 and 1986 respectively) from 1 May 1985 and 23 April in 1986. Stock numbers were adjusted regularly to maintain a constant sward surface height (as measured by HFRO swardstick) of 4 ± 0.5 cm on all treatments. Herbage mass on offer, herbage accumulation and herbage intake were measured by ground level sampling inside and outside exclosure cages every two weeks. The animals were weighed every two weeks.

RESULTS AND DISCUSSION

A summary of the results is given in Table 1 as means of the two nitrogen treatments for the three grass varieties. Highly significant (P<0.001) differences were detected in lamb production from the ryegrass varieties. Averaged over the two seasons lamb production from Aurora was 61% and 34% higher than from S.23 and Meltra respectively. The mean stocking rate necessary to maintain the constant sward height was much greater on the early-flowering Aurora than on the two late-flowering varieties. Herbage accumulation on Aurora during the 34 and 43 day experimental periods in 1985 and 1986 was 59% more than on Meltra and twice that on S.23.

Table 1. Animal and herbage data from three perennial ryegrass varieties during spring (1 May–4 June 1985; 23 April–5 June 1986)

	Aurora	Meltra	S.23	S.E.
Lamb production (kg/ha)				
1985	220	157	126	±6.9
1986	350	270	228	±6.4
Mean stocking rate (ewes/ha)				
1985	24.1	15.3	13.3	±0.91
1986	24.4	17.3	15.3	±0.47
Herbage accumulation (kg DM/ha/day)				
1985	61	34	22	±3.9
1986	46	34	32	±5.4

The results show that the higher pasture production of Aurora which enabled an increase in sheep grazing days of 49% and 69% over Meltra and S.23 respectively would give the farmer the opportunity of reducing his dependence on bought-in feedstuffs, hence improving the efficiency of lamb production from grass.

REFERENCES

DAVIES, D. A., FOTHERGILL, M. and JONES, D. (1986) Assessment of the animal production potential of perennial ryegrass varieties for upland use. In: Frame, J. (ed.) *Grazing, Occasional Symposium No. 19, British Grassland Society*, pp. 201–203.

MUNRO, J. M. M., MAXWELL, T. J. and MORGAN, T. E. H. (1985) Bronydd Mawr Research Centre. *Report of the Welsh Plant Breeding Station for 1984*, pp. 134–144.

Herbage and Lamb Production of Aberystwyth Aurora

W. B. EVANS and
R. V. SCURLOCK
Welsh Plant Breeding
Station, Plas Gogerddan,
Aberystwyth, Dyfed
SY23 3EB, UK

INTRODUCTION

Aurora is a new early-flowering variety of perennial ryegrass bred at the Welsh Plant Breeding Station from plant material collected in the Swiss Alps. Its heading date is 14–18 days earlier than S.24. In small-plot cutting trials it has shown better quality and earlier growth than control varieties, coupled with enhanced winter hardiness and persistency.

A trial has been conducted under lowland conditions to compare its potential herbage and lamb production under continuous grazing with that of established varieties Frances, Talbot and Melle.

EXPERIMENTAL METHODS

The varieties were sown as single variety swards receiving 220 kg N/ha (high N) and as grass–white clover mixtures receiving 90 kg N/ha (low N) in a randomised block replicated three times.

The swards were continuously grazed with Welsh Halfbred ewes and their Suffolk-cross lambs during the pre-weaning period (early April to mid-June) (ratio 1 : 1.67). During the post-weaning period (July to October) Suffolk–cross store lambs were used. Stock numbers were adjusted regularly to maintain a mean sward surface height of 4.0 ± 0.5 cm.

Herbage accumulation was estimated by sampling to ground level under exclosure cages (2 × 1 m). Sward height was monitored regularly using a swardstick. All animals were weighed at regular intervals.

RESULTS

A summary of the herbage and lamb production data for 1985 and 1986 is given in Table 1. Significant differences between varieties were obtained in both herbage and animal production. Since the variety × treatment interactions were

Table 1. Herbage and lamb production – (Mean 1985 and 1986)

	Aurora	Frances	Talbot	Melle	Level of sig.	LSD (P<0.05)
Pre-weaning (early April–3rd week June Herbage organic matter accumulation (kg/ha)	7296	7552	7036	6177	**	445
Lamb live weight gain (g/day)	237	239	225	223	NS	37
(kg/ha)	547	511	515	481	**	31
Post-weaning (mid July–October) Herbage organic matter accumulation (kg/ha)	2994	3345	3122	3275	NS	677
Lamb live weight gain (g/day)	121	94	86	98	*	17
(kg/ha)	409	329	332	334	*	58

non-significant, results for varieties are presented as means for the two treatments.

Herbage organic matter from Melle was significantly lower (P<0.01) than the other varieties during the pre-weaning period but there was no difference during the post-weaning period. Despite having a marginally higher total annual accumulation of herbage, Frances, at the time of introduction of the stock during first week in April, had around 30% less available herbage than Aurora. This allowed 22% more ewe grazing days from Aurora during April.

During the pre-weaning period there was no significant difference between varieties in individual lamb gain but production per hectare was significantly higher on Aurora; the advantage was 7% over Frances and Talbot, and 13% over Melle. This can be related to the higher stock carrying capacity of Aurora in April coupled with its marginally higher herbage quality (+ 2 D units in 1985).

Results for the post-weaning period showed Aurora gave significantly higher gains than the other varieties on individual lamb and per hectare basis. In particular Aurora gave 24% more lamb live weight gain/ha. This apparently was related mainly to the superior quality of Aurora (+ 4 D units in 1985).

CONCLUSIONS

Aurora is superior to the other varieties in terms of lamb production per hectare in spring. Its earlier growth coupled with enhanced quality should enable the farmer to graze earlier and save on concentrates and labour.

Results showed that its enhanced quality from mid-summer onwards also should allow store lambs to be finished earlier.

Annual Output From Grass and Grass–Clover Hill Swards Grazed With Ewes

J. H. McADAM
Agricultural Botany
Research Division,
Department of
Agriculture for N. Ireland
and Department of
Agricultural Botany,
Queen's University,
Newforge Lane, Belfast
BT9 5PX

INTRODUCTION

Clover is agronomically suited to providing the pre-mating nutritional boost (flushing) for hill ewes. However, reseeding inbye and marginal lands (where clover is more likely to succeed) can result in either a sacrifice in production or a considerable time delay before the anticipated final level of output is attained. Such a delay has not been adequately highlighted.

The development of and output from grass and grass–clover swards under sheep grazing are reported below.

MATERIALS AND METHODS

A previously unimproved *Nardus/Festuca* pasture on a peaty podsol at 260 m was ploughed and reseeded in 1980. Plots (18 × 0.12 ha) containing either grass only (perennial ryegrass and Timothy) receiving 180 kg N/ha/annum (as three split dressings) or grass–white clover receiving 60 kg N/ha in spring were grazed continuously with Scottish Blackface ewes from May to August and during October, to herbage mass levels of 2 t/ha (target sward height of 4–6 cm). During autumn swards were stocked with ewes to achieve sward heights of approximately 7 cm at the end of the period.

Sheep were weighed and net herbage accumulation (NHA) was measured using grazing exclusure cages (six per plot) at two weekly intervals and cutting to ground level. Nitrogen fixation was assessed at monthly intervals using the acetylene reduction technique and UME output was calculated using standard tables (MAFF, 1984).

RESULTS AND DISCUSSION

Between 1982 and 1984 herbage production increased from 3.2 to 6.8 t DM/ha on the grass/clover swards and from 4.5 to 6.8 t DM/ha on the grass swards. The contribution made by clover to sward composition (in September) increased from 5% in 1982 to 14% in 1984 with a corresponding rise in net clover accumulation (0.2 t/ha to 0.8 t/ha) and nitrogen fixation (23 to 54 kg N/ha) over the same period. In 1985, persistent rain resulted in poor clover performance, soiling and pasture rejection when animals were stocked to achieve the target heights.

Animal output increased from 1982 to 1984 and only in 1982 was output (kg live weight gain/ha/day) lower in summer from the grass–clover than from the grass swards.

Table 1. Sward performance (A) and sheep performance (B) from grass (G) and grass–clover (G/C) swards between 1982 and 1985

		1982	1983	1984	1985
A. *SWARD PERFORMANCE*					
Production (t DM/ha)	G	4.5	4.5	6.8	5.4
	G/C	3.2	4.5	6.8	6.9
Clover content (%)		5	11	14	8
Clover production (t DM/ha)		0.2	0.5	0.8	0.6
Nitrogen fixation (kg N/ha)		23	29	54	35
B. *SHEEP PERFORMANCE*					
Stocking density (head/ha/day)					
summer	G	29	30	32	38
	G/C	33	34	32	59
autumn	G	31	37	38	42
	G/C	29	36	30	41
Live weight gain (g/head/day)					
summer	G	125	120	130	80
	G/C	104	122	140	50
autumn	G	95	92	62	60
	G/C	118	100	110	60
Output (kg/live weight gain/ha/day)					
summer	G	3.6	3.7	4.2	3.0
	G/C	3.4	4.2	4.5	3.0
autumn	G	3.0	3.4	2.4	2.5
	G/C	3.5	3.6	3.3	2.5
UME output (GJ/ha)					
	G	26.6	35.6	36.7	44.6
	G/C	29.7	36.1	35.1	43.7
Increase in body condition	G		0.03	0.36	0.29
score (Units)	G/C		0.14	0.60	0.51

During October, live weight gain, animal output and body condition score increases were higher from ewes grazing grass–clover than grass swards though stocking densities tended to be higher on the grass than on the grass–clover swards.

The benefits of establishing clover in this situation are clear. Similar, and in many cases higher, levels of output (sward and sheep) were obtained after the second full grazing year from grass–clover swards receiving 120 kg N/ha less than grass swards. Maximum clover content and NHA were not attained until almost four years after sowing and the time delay incurred in achieving the concomitant increases in output and stock carrying capacity must be taken into consideration when integrating an area of improved pasture into the overall farm structure.

REFERENCE

MINISTRY OF AGRICULTURE, FISHERIES AND FOODS (1984). *Energy allowances and feeding systems for ruminants.* Reference Book No. 433, HMSO, London.

Persistency and Contribution to Herbage Yield of White Clover Varieties Under Sheep Grazing

B. G. MERRELL
ADAS, Redesdale EHF,
Rochester, Otterburn,
Newcastle-upon-Tyne,

INTRODUCTION

The white clover content of many hill swards is very low although white clover is included in most hill land seed mixtures. If white clover is to survive under the extreme climatic conditions and the heavy sheep grazing found in the hill situation the selection of winter hardy and persistent white clover varieties is essential. A trial was set up in 1980 to determine the persistency and contribution to yield of a range of white clover varieties grown on peaty hill soil under a sheep grazing regime.

MATERIALS AND METHOD

The trial was sited within a 5 ha hill reseed on 20 cm of peat at 230 m altitude. Eight varieties of white clover (listed in Table 1) were sown with Perma perennial ryegrass in May 1980 in a randomised block design with four replicates. The white clover and perennial ryegrass was sown at 3.9 and 24.7 kg/ha respectively. The trial area received on average 110 kg N, 25 kg P_2O_5 and 60 kg K_2O/ha annually. The nitrogen was applied as two applications, the first 60 kg N/ha in early April and the remainder in late August.

Herbage yields were assessed five times annually using animal exclusion cages. Cuts were taken from two of the four replicates in the four years, 1981–84, and from three replicates in 1985. The first cut was taken in late May and then cuts at approximately monthly intervals to the end of October. A species separation was carried out at each cut.

Botanical analyses were carried out in July using a point quadrat technique. The reseed has been grazed by sheep, and sometimes weaned calves, from mid-April to early December each year and has provided an average 343 livestock unit grazing days per hectare.

RESULTS

Botanical composition

There were large variations between years in white clover content, and percentage ground cover ranged from 9.8 to 31.7% when meaned across all varieties. However, the relative performance of the varieties was consistent over the five years 1981–85.

The SL varieties were the most persistent varieties and contained the highest percentage of white clover and the lowest percentage of "other grasses + weeds".

Table 1. Mean sward composition in July, 1981–85 (% ground cover)

Variety	Leaf type	White clover	Perennial ryegrass	Other grasses + weeds	Bare ground
S184	Small-leaf (SL)	22.0	49.5	26.4	2.1
Kent	Small-leaf (SL)	25.3	47.4	25.1	2.2
Pronitro	Small-leaf (SL)	18.2	49.5	30.5	1.8
Huia	Medium small-leaf (MSL)	13.0	53.2	31.8	2.0
S100	Medium small-leaf (MSL)	15.0	51.9	30.8	2.3
Donna	Medium small-leaf (MSL)	10.8	53.6	33.7	1.9
Menna	Medium small-leaf (MSL)	14.5	50.5	32.9	2.1
Sonya	Medium small-leaf (MSL)	13.6	52.6	31.7	2.1

Dry matter yields

There were large variations between years in clover DM yield which ranged from 465 to 1938 kg/ha, when meaned across all varieties. The SL varieties produced an average 42% more clover DM than the five MSL varieties.

Table 2. Annual white clover DM yield (kg/ha)

Variety	1981	1982	1983	1984	1985
S184	1599	2613	688	820	1014
Kent	1706	2207	583	852	706
Pronitro	952	2141	479	541	693
Huia	670	1417	335	548	572
S100	1097	1966	409	566	683
Donna	678	1355	293	332	549
Menna	942	1716	337	618	736
Sonya	967	2089	596	619	583

Total herbage DM and clover DM yield averaged 8516 and 957 kg/ha respectively, when meaned across all varieties. The contribution of clover DM yield to total herbage DM yield averaged 13.6 and 9.7% for the SL and MSL varieties respectively.

Compared with a pure stand of Perma perennial ryegrass the herbage DM yield from the mixed swards was on average 34% higher, when meaned across all varieties.

Table 3. Mean herbage dry matter yields 1981–85 (kg/ha) and clover content (%)

Clover variety	Total DM yield (kg/ha)	Clover DM yield (kg/ha)	% clover in herbage yield
S184	8591	1347	15.7
Kent	9069	1211	13.4
Pronitro	8111	961	11.8
Huia	8208	708	8.6
S100	8541	944	11.1
Donna	8209	641	7.8
Menna	8571	870	10.2
Sonya	8830	971	11.0

The Effect of Early Defoliation in the Spring by Sheep on the Proportion of Clover in a Grass–White Clover Sward

J. A. LAWS and
J. E. NEWTON
Permanent Grassland
Department, Animal &
Grassland Research
Institute, North Wyke,
Okehampton, Devon
EX20 2SB

The productivity of a grass–white clover sward with minimal input of fertiliser nitrogen is dependent on a substantial presence of clover, at least 20–50% of the dry matter of the sward. An experiment was undertaken to study the effects on the clover proportion of a grass–white clover sward of sheep grazing in the spring, at a time when early lambing flocks turn out to pasture.

The experimental site was in an exposed position on the slowly permeable clayey soils of the Hallsworth series. An area of permanent pasture (predominantly *Agrostis* sp.) which had been oversown with white clover cv. Huia in July 1982 (2.3% clover by weight on 28 February 1984) was grazed by sheep, from either 28 February, 13 March, 27 March or 10 April until 22 May 1984. Sheep numbers were adjusted to maintain a sward height of 25 mm (measured with a rising plate meter; cf. 40 mm measured with a swardstick). At least two sheep were kept on the plots throughout the grazing periods, and a dried grass supplement was offered when necessary, to maintain the target herbage height. The sheep were excluded from part of each treatment area as indicated in Table 1. No nitrogenous fertiliser was applied at any time after the clover was sown in the sward; 60 kg/ha of both phosphate (P_2O_5) and potash (K_2O) was applied in February 1984 in an attempt to ensure that these elements would not limit plant performance.

Measurements of herbage mass and clover proportion were taken on 28 February, at the beginning and end of grazing of each sub-plot, and on 22 May and 26 June 1984.

Table 1. Grazing and regrowth periods (weeks)

Start of grazing (Date)	Length of grazing period (weeks)	Length of regrowth period (weeks)
28 February	4	13
	8	9
	12	5
13 March	4	11
	8	7
	10	5
27 March	4	9
	8	5
10 April	4	7
	6	5

Results showed (Table 2) that there was an increase in herbage yield with increased length of the regrowth period (P<0.001) from the end of grazing to 26 June, but there was no effect on clover proportion.

Table 2. Effect of the length of regrowth period on herbage mass and clover proportion on 26 June 1984

Length of regrowth period Days	Herbage mass t OM/ha	Clover %
92	5.1	29
77	3.6	33
64	3.3	28
50	2.2	22
35	1.5	28
S.E. of treatment means	±0.30	8.0

NB: Data adjusted for the amount of clover present at the end of grazing

The clover proportion of the herbage harvested on 26 June showed a linear trend due to the effect of the date of the start of grazing (Table 3), with the herbage harvested from the areas grazed from the earliest starting date having the highest clover proportion. Similar effects were shown for the length and weight of clover stolon.

Table 3. Effect of date of start of grazing on herbage measurements on 26 June 1984

Start of grazing	Herbage mass 26 June 1984 t. OM/ha	Clover %	Clover Stolon	
			Length m/m²	Weight g/m²
28 February	4.2	29	90	70
13 March	4.1	26	42	35
17 March	4.1	24	76	55
10 April	4.2	19	46	40
S.E. of treatment means	±0.78	±5.0	±18.1	±14.1

NB: Data adjusted for the amount of clover present on 28 February and the different regrowth periods

CONCLUSIONS

— Herbage mass increased with increasing length of the regrowth period from the end of grazing to 26 June, but there was no effect on clover proportion.
— Herbage harvested from the area grazed from 28 February tended to have the highest clover proportion and stolon length on 26 June.
— Early spring grazing of grass–white clover swards is not detrimental to the clover proportion of the sward in June.

LIST OF DELEGATES

Ainsworth, Miss H.
Room 183
Gt Westminster House
Horseferry Road
London SW1P 2AE

Allen, OBE, J. W.
Cover Point
Stainton
Penrith
Cumbria

Anderson, Dr G. D.
Edgerston Tofts
Camptown
Jedburgh TD8 6NF

Appleton, M.
Liscombe EHF
Dulverton
Somerset

Armstrong, R. H.
HFRO
Bush Estate
Penicuik
Midlothian EH26 0PY

Barber, D. D.
ADAS/MAFF
Crown Buildings
Pickering
N Yorkshire

Barratt, N.
Norfolk Agric. Coll.
Easton
Norwich NR9 5DX

Bazley, Miss D. R.
Dept of Zoology
South Parks Road
Oxford OX1 3PS

Bebbington, F.
Lancs Coll. of Agric.
Myerscough Hall
Bilsborrow
Preston
Lancs

Bell, J.
Manor House Farm
Barnard Castle
Teesdale

Bell, Sir J.
Arncliffe Farms
Ingleby Cross
North Allerton
North Yorks

Bolam, P.
Barclays Bank PLC
Juxon House Floor 3
94 St Paul Churchyard
London EC4M 8EH

Booth, I. S.
Clapgate Farm
Field Road
Haslington
Crewe
Cheshire

Branch, D.
Hanwoods Green Farm
Stopham
Pulborough
West Sussex

Brown, S. D.
Farmers Guardian
11 Lennox Drive
Lupset Park
Wakefield WF2 8LL

Burgis, P.
NIAB
Leeds University
Field Station
Headley
Nr Tadcaster
N Yorks

Burra, Mr & Mrs D.
Raisbeck
Orton
Penrith
Cumbria CA10 3SG

Butcher, S. H. K.
Hendersons Cottage
Skipton
N Yorks

Butler, Ms G.
Nutrition Chemistry
ADAS
Kenton Bar
Newcastle NE1 2YA

Carr, F.
Lee Gate Farm
Malham
Skipton
N Yorks

Carr, T. M.
Village Farm Cottage
Notgrove
Cheltenham
Glos

Catton, Mr & Mrs R.
The Shirlings
Westfield Road
Long Crendon
Aylesbury
Bucks

Chaney, Dr K.
Norsk Hydro Ltd
Levington Research
Station
Ipswich
Suffolk

Chestnutt, Dr D. M. B.
Agric. Research Inst.
Hillsborough
Co Down
Northern Ireland

Clark, Dr H.
112 Ashington Grove
Whitley
Coventry CV3 4DE

Clarkson, Prof. M. J.
Leahurst
Liverpool University
Veterinary Field Street
Weston
Wirral

Collis, K. A.
Alfa Laval Agri Ltd
Oakfield
Cwmbran
Gwent NP44 7XP

Cook, J.
WOAD/ADAS
Station Road
Ruthin
Clwyd
Wales

Corrall, A. J.
The Secretary
BGS
c/o AGRI
Hurley
Maidenhead
Berks SL6 5LR

Crabtree, J.
Bolton Park Farm
Bolton Abbey
Nr Skipton
N Yorks

Craig, Mr & Mrs A. B.
Limepark
Armoy
Co Antrim
Northern Ireland

Crichton, Mrs J. M.
BGS Office
c/o AGRI
Hurley
Maidenhead
Berks SL6 5LR

Cunningham, Prof. J. M. M.
WOSCA
Auchincruive
Ayr KA6 5HW

Daly, M.
UKF Fertilisers Ltd
Ince
Chester CH2 4LB

Dampney, P.
ADAS
Kenton Bar
Newcastle upon Tyne

Davies, Miss A. G.
WPBS
Plas Gogerddan
Aberystwyth
Dyfed SY23 3EB
Wales

Davies, D. A.
WPBS
Plas Gogerddan
Aberystwyth
Dyfed S23 3EB

Davies, M. H.
Redesdale EHF
Rochester
Otterburn
Newcastle upon Tyne

Davies, T. W.
ADAS
Woodthorn
Wergs Road
Wolverhampton

Davies, W. I. C.
ADAS/Welsh Office
Trawsgoed
Aberystwyth
Dyfed SY23 4HT

Duley, Mrs L. A.
MAFF/ADAS
Block C
Government Buildings
Whittington Road
Worcester WR5 2LG

Eadie, J.
HFRO
Bush Estate
Penicuik
Midlothian
Scotland

Edwards, H. M.
MAFF
Agricola House
Gilwilly Estate
Penrith
Cumbria

Elliot, J.
Rawburn
Duns
Berwickshire
Scotland

Etherton, P.
Greentrees Farm
Balcombe Forest
Sussex

Evans, B.
ADAS
Penrallt
Caernarfon
Gwynedd
Wales

Evans, W. B.
WPBS
Plas Gogerddan
Aberystwyth
Dyfed SY23 3EB

Farquharson, Mr & Mrs K. G.
Kinclune
Kirriemuir
Angus DD8 5HX

Finch, I.
The Old Rectory
Ilketshall
St Andrews
Beccles
Suffolk

Fisher, I. L.
59 Rounds Hill
Kenilworth
Warwickshire CV8 1DW

Flanagan, Dr. S
The Agric. Institute
Belclare
Tuam
Co Galway
Ireland

Foster, M. J.
Arncliffe Cote
Arncliffe
Skipton
N Yorks

Gaunt, R.
Carlshead Farms
Paddock House Lane
Sicklinghall
Wetherby
N Yorks

Gillam, T. A.
Wheatlands Farm
Roecliffe
N Boroughbridge
N Yorks YO5 9ND

Goldie, T. S.
ICI Agric. Division
PO Box 1
Billingham
Cleveland

Gooding, R. F.
Agric. Dept
W. Scotland Agric. Coll.
Ayr
Scotland

Gould, Mr & Mrs R. D.
WOAD/ADAS
Crown Offices
Canal Bank
Brecon
Powys
Wales LD3 7HL

Graham, Mr S.
Adamsdorse Farm
Thorpe Satchwell
Melton Mowbray

Grant, Miss S. A.
HFRO
Bush Estate
Penicuik
Midlothian EH26 0PY

Green, Mr & Mrs J.
Church Farm
Towersy
Thame
Oxon

Greenwood, D. R.
Barhan
Heasley Mill
South Molton
Devon

Griffiths, Miss M. S.
Trawsgoed EHF
Aberystwyth
Dyfed SY23 4HT
Wales

Griffiths, W. D. E.
Rumenco Ltd
Stretton House
Derby Road
Burton-on-Trent
Staffs

Gunn, Dr. R. G.
HFRO
Bush Estate
Penicuik
Midlothian EH26 0PY

Hall, J.
Dalston
Carlisle
Cumbria

Harvey, Miss A.
AGRI
Hurley
Maidenhead
Berks SL6 5LR

Hewetson, C. J.
Pasture House
Broughton
Skipton
N Yorks BD23 3AH

Hewetson, J. A.
3 Oxford Terrace
Carlton
Skipton
N. Yorks

Holliday, L. B.
Mount St John
Thirsk
York YO7 2DT

Hunt, D.
c/o 4743 West 7 Avenue
Vancouver
British Columbia
Canada VGT 1CT

Jefferys, Mr & Mrs P.
Watergate
Wark
Hexham
Northumberland

Johnson, J.
MAFF/ADAS
Block 2
Government Buildings
Lawnswood
Leeds

Rhys Jones, D.
WPBS
Plas Gogerddan
Aberystwyth
Dyfed S23 4EB
Wales

Jones, J. R.
WPBS
Plas Gogerddan
Aberystwyth
Dyfed SY23 3EB

Jones, Mr & Mrs P. L.
Home Farm
Overton-on-Dee
Wrexham
Clwyd
Wales

Jones, R.
Sheep Unit
NAC
Stoneleigh
Kenilworth
Warwickshire

Jordan, Dr W. J.
NIAB
Huntingdon Road
Cambridge

Kay, H. R. R.
ICI PLC
Beckside Farm
Ivegill
Carlisle

Keeling, Dr B. J.
Animal Husbandry Division
N Scotland Agric. Coll.
581 King Street
Aberdeen

Kynge, Major J. J.
Fox & Hounds Farm
Carlton-in-Cleveland
N Yorks

Laws, J. A.
PGDI
AGRI
North Wyke
Okehampton
Devon EX20 2SB

Laycock, Ms K.
Nutrition Chemistry
ADAS
Kenton Bar
Newcastle NE1 2YA

Lewis, Dr G. E. D.
3 Newton Grove
Bedford Park
London W4

Lister, Dr C. J.
MAFF/ADAS
Olantigh Road
Wye
Ashford
Kent TN25 5EL

Lloyd, Ms M.
E Scotland Coll. Agric.
APAD
Bush Estate
Penicuik
Midlothian
Scotland

Lohoar, J.
Drumcarro Farm
Cupar
Fife KY15 5TY

Love, Miss L.
Forum Feeds
Forum House
Brighton Road
Redhill
Surrey

Mackie, C. K.
N Scotland Agric. Coll.
581 King Street
Aberdeen AB9 1UD
Scotland

Mackie, Mr & Mrs D. L.
Frome Manor Farm,
Bishops Frome
Nr Worcester
Worcestershire WR6 5BB

Maclay, The Lord
Duchal
Kilmacolm
Renfrewshire
Scotland

Mair, A. J.
Home Farm
Borden
Sittingbourne
Kent

Mann, Miss D.
c/o David Norgate
Usk College
Usk
Gwent
Wales

Marsden, M. T.
Bull House Lodge
Penistone
S Yorks

Marsh, A.
Carlshead Farms
Paddock House Lane
Sicklinghall
Wetherby
N Yorks

Maxwell, Dr T. J.
HFRO
Bush Estate
Penicuik
Midlothian
Scotland

McAdam, J. H.
Dept. Agric. for Northern Ireland
Newforge Lane
Belfast BT9 5PX
Northern Ireland

McCall Smith, L.
Connachan
Crieff
Scotland

McClelland, T. H.
ESCA
Bush Estate
Penicuik
Midlothian EH26 0QE

McDougall, K. A.
Chalk Hill
Warham
Wells-next-the-Sea
Norfolk NR23 1NS

McGaughey, G.
Dept Agric. for Northern Ireland
Newforge Lane
Belfast BT9 5PX
Northern Ireland

McKay, B.
Green Plains
Martletwy
Narberth
Dyfed SA67 8AH

Merrell, B.
Redesdale EHF
Rochester
Otterburn
Newcastle upon Tyne

Milne, Dr J. A.
HFRO
Bush Estate
Penicuik
Midlothian
Scotland

Minter, C. M.
Harper Adams
Agric. Coll.
Newport
Shropshire

Mitchell, F.
HFRO
Bush Estate
Penicuik
Midlothian EH26 0PY

Mowat, D. L.
74 Somerset Avenue
Galmington
Taunton
Somerset

Munro, J. M. M.
Bronydd Mawr
Research Station
Nr Trecastle
Brecon
Powys

Nelson, D. L.
Glensaugh
Laurencekirk
Kincardineshire

Nelson, Mr & Mrs J. K.
4 Wood Drive
Brittains Lane
Sevenoaks
Kent TN13 2NL

Newton, R. J.
Laneley House
Roberttown
Liversedge
W Yorks

Owen, B.
ICI PLC
Alderley Park
Macclesfield
Cheshire SK10 4TG

Owen, E. G.
Fron
Llanbrynmair
Powys SY19 7AW

Parker, J. W. G.
ADAS
c/o AGRI
Hurley
Maidenhead
Berks SL6 5LR

Parry, J.
Farming News
8 Beechwood Crescent
Harrogate HG2 0PA

Payne, M.
Hendersons Cottage
Skipton
N Yorks

Penning, P. D.
AGRI
Hurley
Maidenhead
Berks SL6 5LR

Peto, F.
Cowdenknowes Mains
Earlston
Berwickshire
Scotland

Pollott, G. E.
MLC
PO Box 44
Queensway House
Bletchley
Milton Keynes
Bucks MK2 2EF

Povey, Miss G. M.
Dept Agric.
The University
Newcastle upon Tyne NE1 7RU

Pritchard, Mr & Mrs P. A.
New Cottage
Bickley
Newnham Bridge
Tenbry Wells
Worcestershire

Rawlins, Miss F. A.
PGD
AGRI
North Wyke
Okehampton
Devon

Recordon, Miss E.
Bush Farm
Colwall
Nr Malvern
Worcestershire WR13 6HH

Robinson, S.
WCF Ltd
Alanbrooke Road
Rosehill Trading Estate
Carlisle
Cumbria

Rowlinson, A. J.
FSL Bells Ltd
Hartham
Corsham
Wiltshire

Sibbald, A.
HFRO
Bush Estate
Penicuik
Midlothian
Scotland

Sim, D. A.
HFRO
Bush Estate
Penicuik
Midlothian EH26 0PY

Simpkin, P. G.
Dalgety Agric.
Walton-le-Dale
Preston

Slade, Mr & Mrs C. F. R.
ADAS
Woodthorne
Wolverhampton WV6 8TQ

Smales, Mr & Mrs J. C.
Thornton
Berwick upon Tweed TD15 2LP

Smith, D.
Sydney Farm
Halstock
Yeovil
Somerset

Speedy, A. W.
University of Oxford
Agric. Sci. Building
Parks Road
Oxford OX1 3PF

Stephenson, J.
4 Brookfield
Hampsthwaite
Harrogate HG3 2EF

Stuart, A.
Aberdona House
Alloa
Clackmannanshire FK10 3QP

Swift, G.
E Scotland Agric. Coll.
CPAD
Bush Estate
Penicuik
Midlothian
Scotland

Tait, Dr R. M.
4743 West 7 Avenue
Vancouver
British Columbia
Canada

Taylor, Miss A. R.
Big Farm Weekly
100 Avenue Road
London NW3 3TP

Tempest, Dr W. M.
Harper Adams
Agric. Coll.
Newport
Shropshire

Thorley, J.
The Secretary
NSA
106 High Street
Tring
Herts HP23 4AF

Thorpe, E. F.
Seale Hayne Coll.
Newton Abbott
Devon

Tiley, Dr G. E. D.
Agronomy Dept
W Scotland Agric. Coll.
Auchincruive
Ayr
Scotland

Tilly, N.
1 Glenview Cottages
Great Corby
Carlisle

Towle, Miss A. S.
Rumenco Ltd
Stretton House
Derby Road
Burton-on-Trent
Staff

Treacher, Dr T. T.
AGRI
Hurley
Maidenhead
Berks SL6 5LR

Tweed, C. W.
Corkermaine
40 Ballycoose Road
Ballygally
Larne
Co Antrim
Northern Ireland

Usher, Mr & Mrs C. J.
Courthill
Hawick
Roxburghshire
Scotland

Wardrop, Mr & Mrs J. C.
Harden Mains
Jedburgh TD8 6RB
Scotland

Waterhouse, Dr A.
WSAC
University Stirling
Stirling
Scotland

Watson, D.
Fough Farm
Longnor
Nr Buxton

Webster, Dr. G. M.
Dept of Agric.
The University
Newcastle upon Tyne NE1 7RU

Webster, Mr & Mrs S.
Friars Hurst
North Stainley
Ripon HG4 3JD

Weir, Dr A.
National Park
Authority
Eastburn
South Park
Hexham

Whiteford, I.
Hilltarvit Mains
Cupar
Fife
Scotland

Wilkins, Dr R. J.
PGD
AGRI
North Wyke
Okehampton
Devon

Williams, D. W.
Nickerson Seed Specialist Ltd
Stow Bardolph
King's Lynn
Norfolk

Wrench, Mr & Mrs J.
Beeches Farm
Saltney Ferry
Chester CH4 0BW

Wright, Mr & Mrs P. J.
16 Trimnells, Colerne
Chippenham
Wiltshire SN14 8EP

Young, N. E.
PGD
AGRI
North Wyke
Okehampton
Devon

Additional Registrations

Barratt, H. W.
Hilltop Farm
Leathley
Otley
W Yorks LS21 2LG

Vincent, G.
Manor Farm
Upton
Peterborough
Cambs

Cluley, Miss J.
3 Meadowfield Close
Easingwold
York YO6 3DP

Dale, I.
Mount Leven Farm
Leven Bank
Yarm
Cleveland

Meeres, J.
Mount Leven Farm
Leven Bank
Yarm
Cleveland

Handley, R.
V. J. S. Leslie & Partners
Kingsway Veterinary Centre
Skipton
Yorks

Orr, R.
AGRI
Hurley
Maidenhead
Berks SL6 5LR

Watson, J. R.
18 Dukes Road
Hexham
Northumberland NE46 3AW

Hart, E.
Vince Moor East
Dalton-on-Tees
Darlington DL2 2PN

Lodge, R.
Royds Farm
Elsecar
S Yorks